ATOMISM IN ENGLAND
FROM HARIOT TO NEWTON

Oxford University Press, Ely House, London W. 1

GLASGOW NEW YORK TORONTO MELBOURNE WELLINGTON
CAPE TOWN SALISBURY IBADAN NAIROBI LUSAKA ADDIS ABABA
BOMBAY CALCUTTA MADRAS KARACHI LAHORE DACCA
KUALA LUMPUR HONG KONG TOKYO

ATOMISM IN ENGLAND
FROM HARIOT
TO NEWTON

by
ROBERT HUGH KARGON

Department of the History of Science
The Johns Hopkins University

CLARENDON PRESS
OXFORD
1966

© Oxford University Press 1966

Printed in Great Britain by Spottiswoode, Ballantyne & Co. Ltd., London and Colchester

To Marcia and Jeremy

This work was completed with the aid of the
AMERICAN PHILOSOPHICAL SOCIETY

PREFACE

THE atomic doctrine has, with good reason, always interested historians of science. It affords an excellent example of the use of a systematic hypothesis to explain natural phenomena. The atomic philosophy, in varying form, has been found useful from Greek antiquity until the present day.

In the seventeenth century, atomism played a particularly important scientific role. The rise of the mechanical philosophy, the doctrine that all phenomena can be explained by matter and its motion, was a significant part of the 'scientific revolution'. Atomism was a mechanical philosophy which, along with Cartesianism, captured the imagination of the natural philosophers of the seventeenth century and replaced the moribund Aristotelian world-view. The history of atomism, therefore, provides a case study in the rise of a new world-picture, so different from the scholasticism of the previous centuries, and so close to our own. The establishment of the mechanical philosophy was a conceptual revolution of the first magnitude, and one which offers the historian valuable lessons.

In the light of its undisputed importance, it is surprising that the historians of atomism are almost all 'ahistorical'. They tend to remove the ideas and concepts of atomism from their historical context; most historians of atomism (see bibliography) deal with their subject as if it existed, so to speak, in a void. In these works, atomism is treated as an ideological development of a few major figures. Absent are truly *historical* relations between men and ideas; all stress is placed upon internal philosophical and scientific developments. The secondary figures who were crucial to the reception and dissemination of atomistic doctrines are either ignored or mentioned only in passing. Atomism becomes a concept developed by philosophical titans and not *real men,* facing *real problems*—social, political, theological, and personal, as well as scientific.

I do not deny that an ahistorical approach can be revealing, even in intellectual history. The standard history of atomism is Kurd Lasswitz' excellent *Geschichte der Atomistik*. Lasswitz' work is a remarkable achievement. Primarily, it is a study of the advances made in the atomic doctrine, without emphasis upon the historical relations between the men who were the incarnations of the ideas. Still, the *Geschichte der Atomistik* merits great respect for its invaluable insights and admirable scholarship.

My essay will attempt to accomplish two objectives. First, I wish to bring to the attention of historians of science the existence and importance of two circles of natural philosophers (the Northumberland and Newcastle groups) which played an important role in the history of atomism. Secondly, I wish to trace the evolution of atomism and illustrate the mechanism of its establishment in England in the latter seventeenth century. In doing so, I will re-evaluate the contributions of four major figures (Hariot, Bacon, Boyle, and Newton) and many minor ones, including Walter Charleton, the Duke and Duchess of Newcastle, William Petty, Charles Cavendish, and John Pell. My story will close with an examination of the relationship between atomism and the thought of the young Newton, and with the firm establishment of atomism in England as a respectable natural philosophy.

There are many people to whom I owe a debt of thanks. My friends and colleagues, David Kubrin and Wilbur Applebaum, have been two delightful and needed critics. I should like to give special thanks to Professor L. P. Williams for his warmly appreciated personal guidance and insights into the history of science. My greatest debt, of course, is owed to Professor Henry Guerlac who has made liberally available to me his vast fund of historical sophistication. If I may call myself an historian of science, it is to Professor Guerlac that I owe that pleasure. Finally, I must thank my wife Marcia for her unflagging devotion to the seventeenth century.

This work was completed with the support of the University of Illinois Summer Faculty Fellowship and with the aid of a grant from the American Philosophical Society.

CONTENTS

I
ATOMISM AND ARISTOTELIANISM

By THE beginning of the seventeenth century, the remnants of the medieval English world were rapidly disappearing, put to an early demise by the bold discoveries of new lands, by rapidly changing economic and social relations of agriculture and incipient industry, and by equally bold and rapidly changing intellectual adventures; as the old order passed away, the Aristotelian world-view was loosening its grasp, shaken by the prodding of searchers into new paths. In a fashion similar to that of other areas, the Aristotelian mode of natural philosophy now faced serious threats.

The scientific views of the sixteenth-century Peripatetics were swiftly becoming unsuitable for the needs of natural philosophers. The new investigators of nature emphasized mechanical causes and the utility and power of experimental learning; for these men, the scholastic methods of philosophizing were deemed inadequate. In 1661, for example, Joseph Glanvill epitomized the entire seventeenth century's objections to Aristotelianism: it was merely 'verbal', it gave no satisfying account of the phenomena, and it led to no new discoveries 'for the *use* of common Life'.[1]

From the end of the sixteenth century until the middle of the seventeenth, Aristotelian scientific explanation was attacked on these same grounds. From the very first, there were some scientists who rejected the forms and qualities of the Peripatetics and turned to a more 'mechanical' philosophy: the explanation of phenomena in terms of the mechanics of matter and motion. One such philosophy was the atomic doctrine.

Almost all histories of atomism or of the mechanical philosophy in general treat of the debate between the Aristotelians and the new philosophers as if the former were nameless, shapeless shades. It was, of course, not so. Aristotelianism was institutionalized in the universities and taught through 'modern' textbooks as well as through the works of Aristotle. Perhaps the most important of these texts for natural philosophy was the *Physica Peripatetica*,[2] of Johannes Magirus, an author whom Isaac Newton studied at Cambridge during his student years.[3]

According to Magirus, visible matter is composed of a *materia prima,* an unformed matter existing as the principle of pure potentiality. In it, the

---

[1] Joseph Glanvill, *Scepsis Scientifica, or the Vanity of Dogmatizing,* ed. John Owen (London, 1885), p. 127
[2] Johannes Magirus, *Physica Peripatetica* (Frankfurt, 1597).
[3] Cambridge University Add. MSS. 3996, ff. 16–26.

actuating principles or *forms* are substantial, produced in all generations
and destroyed in all corruptions, which produce by their presence all the
qualities found in the natural world. In particular, matter exists in this world
as four elements—air, earth, fire, and water—with which are associated
various qualities of two basic kinds. First, there are the 'manifest' qualities
which are 'evident and easy to understand'.[1] Secondly, there are 'obscure'
or 'occult' qualities such as magnetic and electrical attraction which are not
so easily classified. Of the *manifest* qualities there are again two types: primary and secondary. The primary qualities, four in number, are directly
associated with the four elements; the secondary qualities are compounded
of them. The primary qualities include hotness, coldness, wetness, and
dryness. Some secondary qualities are colour, odour, taste, rarity, density,
levity, gravity, hardness, and softness. The mechanical philosophy did not,
as is sometimes supposed, create the distinction between primary and
secondary qualities; it did, however, relegate the Peripatetic *primary*
qualities to the ranks of *secondary* qualities.

Another excellent example of seventeenth-century Aristotelianism is the
Corps de philosophie of Scipion du Pleix.[2] Natural phenomena, according to
Scipion (following Aristotle's *De Generatione et Corruptione*), can be explained
by the twin principles of form and matter. One must distinguish between
first or prime matter, and secondary matter. 'Prime matter is the first
principle of natural things.'[3] It is the principle of pure potentiality or recep-
tivity, without any forms or qualities whatever. Prime matter cannot be
found in nature; it must be discovered by reason alone. Second matter is
matter found in nature. It is matter enformed with all the observable
qualities noted in experience.

Natural bodies are composed of four 'elements' which are formed from
the union of four primary qualities in matter. The four qualities are heat,
cold, dryness, and wetness. Heat and cold are 'active' qualities, wetness and
dryness merely passive. Fire combines the qualities of heat, dryness; air is
wet and hot; water is cold and wet; earth is dry and cold. The character of
the elements depends both on the forms of qualities themselves and the
nature of their union with matter. For example, water is wetter than air
because its matter is denser (*grossière*), and presumably the union of form
and matter more complete. Similarly, red-hot iron is hotter even than fire,
because the matter of iron is crass, dense, and solid. Secondary qualities of
bodies, such as lightness, heaviness, softness, hardness, etc. depend upon
the combination of elements and their associated primary qualities.[4]

This system of substantial forms and qualities was only with difficulty
applied to physical problems by scientists in the late sixteenth and early

[1] Magirus, p. 89.   [2] Scipion du Pleix, *Corps de philosophie* (Geneva, 1645).
[3] Ibid., p. 50.   [4] Ibid., pp. 242–8.

seventeenth centuries who lived in a world quite different from that of St. Thomas, Magirus' great predecessor. The men of the new age, becoming increasingly accustomed to the presence of machinery and mechanical implements within the compass of their common experience found the Aristotelian explanations mere collections of words, i.e. obvious tautologies. To account for the attraction of iron by the loadstone, for example, the scholastic Puteanus maintained that:

[The magnet attracts from] its substantial form as from a prime motor and self-motor, and as from its own most potent nature and its natural temperament.[1]

This type of explanation increasingly became foreign to scientists who by 1600 were being trained not nearly so thoroughly in scholastic discourse as in mathematics or in the crafts. These men turned from scholastic classification, and using the analogies of the world around them, turned toward that form of explanation which relied upon the impact or contact of matter with matter. Some, for example, returned to Epicurus' notion of a corporeal magnetic effluvium which, returning to the loadstone, draws the iron to it.[2]

Why did many of the new philosophers of the seventeenth century turn to atomism, and in particular to the atomism of Epicurus and Lucretius? The question is, unfortunately, too complex to be settled here. There are, however, certain correspondences between the needs of the natural philosophers and the mode of explanation put forth by the ancient atomists. The ancients had explained phenomena on the basis of the size, shape, and motion of particles of matter. This doctrine appealed to the scientists of the seventeenth century for several reasons. First, the causal relationship posited by atomism was close to their experiences with gross bodies. In the visible world, bodies are moved by pressure or collision of matter with matter. The machines involved in the new industries provided certain of the analogies, utilizing impact or the presence of a vacuum.[3] Secondly, after a mechanical explanation was decided upon, a sub-visible mechanism was necessary in order to provide such an explanation for those phenomena that were patently non-mechanical at the visible level. For example, the attraction of a magnet for iron had to be explained by an 'invisible' mechanism if one were to abandon the Aristotelian hypothesis for a mechanical one. Atomism provided an easy, systematic, and palatable solution for all these problems. Thirdly, the revival of classical atomism can be viewed also within the framework of the humanist tradition; it was very natural for

[1] Quoted in William Gilbert, *On the Loadstone*, trans. P. F. Mottelay (n.p., 1892), pp. 101–2.

[2] Ibid., pp. 100–1.

[3] Henry Percy, *Advice to his Son*, ed. G. B. Harrison (London, 1920), p. 69. Henceforth cited as *Advice*.

philosophers to return to classical texts for inspiration and ideas. Humanism and atomism are, of course, not *essentially* related. The latter did, however, use humanist techniques when convenient. Finally, there were new experimental advances such as the Torricellian vacuum and certain chemical problems which Aristotelianism found it difficult to treat in a satisfactory manner.[1]

The new atomists could not, of course, merely resurrect ancient atomism. The new atomic doctrine had to incorporate within it the experimental advances for the sake of which, in part, it was revived. At first the atomic theory was used to solve particular difficulties in the explanation of natural phenomena, as for example in the early work of Thomas Hariot. Some, like Daniel Sennert and Nicholas Hill, tried to bridge the gap between atomism and Aristotelianism with attempts at synthesis. Finally, others like Pierre Gassend and the corpuscularians Thomas Hobbes and René Descartes built great entire systems, going far beyond their classical predecessors in wealth of detail.

The history of atomism as part of the establishment of the mechanical philosophy provides an excellent case study in the transition from one world-view to another. The atomic hypothesis was, moreover, viewed by many early scientists of the seventeenth century as a vital part of their work. The greatest scientific minds of the age were engaged in an elaboration and modernization of the doctrine. The purpose of the following chapters will be to examine that part of the history of atomism which unfolded in seventeenth-century England.

[1] R. Hooykaas, 'Experimental Origin of Chemical Atomic and Molecular Theory Before Boyle', *Chymia* 2 (1949) 65–80.

II

THE WIZARD EARL
AND THE NEW SCIENCE

IN THE late sixteenth century, scientific learning was primarily encouraged and financed by wealthy amateurs who gave their time and patronage to the advancement of the new philosophy. The greatest of the earlier English 'virtuosi' was Henry Percy, the ninth Earl of Northumberland, known as the 'Wizard Earl'. Born of an important and wealthy, though ill-starred, family, Percy had a share in the advance of science through his patronage of an entire school of natural philosophers. His range was not, however, limited to science; his interests extended to poetry and drama as well. As Alexander Read later described him, he was 'the favourer of all good learning, and the Mecaenas of learned men'.[1]

The Percy family was one of the richest and most powerful feudal families of England.[2] It was often said that 'the North knows no king but a Percy'.[3] While it is true that the traditional seat of Percy power was in the northern shires, by the mid-sixteenth century the family held extensive estates in eight counties. Their lands grew considerably under the proprietorship of Thomas Percy, the seventh Earl of Northumberland. When the seventh earl, the uncle of the Wizard, was executed in August 1572, for his role in the rising of 1569,[4] the title reverted to his brother, Henry. The new leader of the Percy family, the eighth earl, was the father of eight sons by Catherine Neville. His eldest, Henry, was born at Tynemouth Castle in 1564. The eighth earl was politically suspect; in 1585 he was arrested, and he died in the Tower under mysterious circumstances.[5] Thus, at the age of 21, the younger Henry Percy became the ninth earl of Northumberland, seventh in the line to the throne of England, and the possessor of a considerable fortune.

The sources of the Percy fortune play an interesting and not unimportant role in the early history of the new science. By the mid-sixteenth century, the Percys, as great landowners, participated in the rapid changes in the agricultural society of England. As the manorial system was gradually

[1] Alexander Read, *Chirurgicall Lectures of Tumors and Ulcers* (London, 1935), p. 307.
[2] Percy. *Advice*, p. 7.
[3] G. R. Batho, 'Percies at Petworth (1574–1632)', *Suss. Arch. Coll.* **95** (1957) 2. Henceforth cited as 'Petworth'.
[4] Ibid., pp. 2–3.
[5] Edmund Lodge, *Portraits of Illustrious Personages of Great Britain* (London, 1835), vol. 1.

replaced by a 'capitalist' rural economy, and as large areas of land began to become affected by enclosures in the sixteenth century, new relationships developed between lord and tenant.[1] The feudal lord became a landlord in the modern sense. The lord was, therefore, cut free from the land. He no longer was forced to remain an active agriculturist. Indeed, the Percys are an example of this trend. Although their great sources of income were in the north, by 1574 the Percys shifted their chief residence to Petworth in Sussex.[2] It is important to note that the Wizard Earl was an absentee land-lord *par excellence*. Henry Percy was the first who rarely even visited his northern lands.[3] Equally importantly, the use of money first became universal in the mix-sixteenth century.[4] The Percys drew rents, in money, from their estates. The head of the Percy house was, therefore, given the liberty to employ his time as he willed and in addition, he was given a surplus income (a net of £12,000) sufficient to support his scientific whims. It has long been recognized that in the days before professional scientists, the existence of men of means and leisure was a necessary condition for the growth of science.[5] The social and economic changes of the sixteenth century[6] supplied Percy with this leisure, and in addition gave him resources with which to subsidize an entire circle of savants. Without Percy's endowment, much of the work of Thomas Hariot, for example, would have been impossible.

The Wizard Earl's personality particularly fitted him for his role as patron of the arts and sciences. He was educated by private tutors, and developed as 'naturally a kind of inward and reserved man'.[7] After a sporting youth, he came to prefer philosophy and 'this infinite worthy mistress' knowledge to any finite mistress'.[8] In his pursuit of knowledge, he kept a splendid library, spending over £50 per annum on books alone. He also gathered around him some of the most sparkling intellects of England, including Thomas Hariot, mathematician, physicist, and astronomer; Robert Hues, the author of *De globorum usu*; Walter Warner, mathematician and physicist; Robert Norton, the translator of Stevin; John Donne;[9] and

[1] R. H. Tawney, *The Agrarian Problem in the Sixteenth Century* (London, 1912), p. 180. Henceforth cited as *Problem*.

[2] Batho, 'Petworth', pp. 1–28.

[3] Henry Percy, *Household Papers*, ed. G. R. Batho (London, 1962), p. xviii.

[4] Tawney, *Problem*, p. 186

[5] See for example the remarks of Alexandre Koyré in *Scientific Change*, ed. A. C. Crombie (New York, 1963), p. 854.

[6] For these, see Tawney, *Problem*, and Peter Ramsey, *Tudor Economic Problems* (London, 1963).

[7] B. M. Hargreave MSS. 226, f. 241, quoted in G. R. Batho, 'The Library of the Wizard Earl: Henry Percy, Ninth Earl of Northumberland', *Library* 15, 5th series (1960) 246. Henceforth cited as 'Library'.

[8] Ibid., p. 246.

[9] E. Gosse, *Life and Letters of John Donne* (London, 1899), I, 100–2.

dramatists and poets, like Chapman and Peel; Christopher Marlowe too is often included in this list.[1] Sir Walter Ralegh, a good friend of Percy, Ferdinando Stanley, and Lord George Hunsdon likewise were among the men who, at various times, gathered around the Earl of Northumberland.[2] Other members of note included Nathanael Torporley, the mathematician Thomas Allen, and Nicholas Hill.[3]

Except for some small works of Torporley, Hill, and Hues, nothing of scientific interest was published by the group while it was in existence. To reconstruct the philosophical atmosphere and doctrines of the circle is therefore difficult. Nevertheless, from the fragmentary information which has filtered down to us, something about their views can be established. First, the 'scientific' members of the group—Percy, Hariot, Warner, Torporley, Hill, and Hues—were all Copernicans. Secondly, with the exception of Torporley,[4] they were also avowed atomists. The two views are linked in one very important respect: both were phases of a concerted attack upon Aristotelian natural philosophy. To be sure, the members of the 'Northumberland Circle' were not the only critics of Aristotle in late sixteenth- and early seventeenth-century England,[5] but they were, as far as can be determined at present, the only English school to combine Copernicanism with that complete rejection of Aristotelianism which accompanies acceptance of the atomic philosophy of Democritus, Epicurus, and Lucretius.

As the late F. R. Johnson has so admirably shown, the Aristotelian framework of natural philosophy underwent severe attack in late sixteenth-century England at the hands of astronomers and mathematicians.[6] Yet properly speaking, it was late scholasticism that was being criticized; the attitude of the new natural philosophers toward Aristotle himself was, at best, ambivalent. While denying his supreme authority and attacking his views of astronomy and cosmology, they respected the Stagirite, and adopted his modes of explanation in almost all other areas. Excellent examples of this ambivalence can be found in the writings of John Dee, Thomas Digges, and William Gilbert. The work of these three deserves

[1] See, for example, John Bakeless, *Tragicall History of Christopher Marlowe* (Cambridge, Mass., 1939), I, 134–7.

[2] Percy, *Advice*, p. 10.

[3] Anthony à Wood, *Athenae Oxonienses*, ed. Philip Bliss (London, 1812–20), I, 542.

[4] No information is available at present on the views of Hues and Allen.

[5] See for example, F. R. Johnson, *Astronomical Thought in Renaissance England* (Baltimore, 1937). Henceforth cited as *Thought*; Johnson, 'Thomas Digges, the Copernican System and the Idea of the Infinity of the Universe in 1576', *Huntington Library Bulletin*, No. 5 (1934), pp. 69–117; Johnson and Sanford Larkey, 'Robert Recorde's Mathematical Teaching and the Anti-Aristotelian Movement', *Huntington Library Bulletin* No. 7 (1935) pp. 59–87.

[6] Johnson, *Thought, passim*.

2

some attention as the several currents running throughout their writings, taken together, give a glimpse into the scientific milieu of which the Northumberland Circle formed a part.

John Dee (1527–1608) was a leading participant in the Platonic-Pythagorean revival of the English renaissance. Dee's number mysticism, best exemplified by his acceptance of the dictum that the soul is a number moving itself,[1] was balanced by a strong respect for 'experiment'. His goal was not mere speculation, but rather the 'knowledg Sensible and Experimentall of Archimedes',[2] which marked the fusion of mathematics and experience.

This art teachesth to bring to actuall experience, sensible, all working conclusions by all the Arts Mathematicall purposed and by true Naturall Philosophie concluded. . . . And because it proceedeth by *Experiences* and searcheth forth the causes of Conclusions by *Experiences*: and also putteth the Conclusions themselves in Experience, it is named of some *Scientia Naturalis*. The *Experimental Science*, Nicolaus Cusanus termeth it so in his *Experiments Staticall*.[3]

There is no direct evidence that Dee ever accepted the physical reality of the Copernican system. Indeed, in his 'Mathematical Preface' he appears to adhere to the Aristotelian doctrine, assuming a stationary earth.[4] Despite his Pythagoro-Platonism, Dee was very much an Aristotelian. Just as he drew no sharp line between theory and experience, he did not distinguish sharply between Platonism and Aristotelianism. Mathematics, he claimed, was necessary for 'all manner of Philosophie Academicall or Peripateticall'.[5] Dee tried to apply mathematics and 'experiment' *within* the old Aristotelian framework. Using the basic scholastic categories of substantial and accidental forms, Dee attempted to 'quantify' the scholastic *mixtio* relating forms and qualities.[6]

Dee's pupil, Thomas Digges, was, however, one of the more influential Copernicans.[7] His book, *Perfit Description of the Coelestiall Orbes,* went through at least six editions within twenty years of its appearance in 1576. Digges followed Dee in attacking the notion of the infallibility of the Stagirite. Like Dee, Digges also can in many respects be termed an Aristotelian. 'I cannot a little commende the modestie of that grave Philosopher

---

[1] John Dee, 'Mathematical Preface' to Euclid, *Elements of Geometrie,* trans. H. Billingsley (London, 1570), sig. iv. Henceforth cited as 'Preface'.

[2] Dee, 'Preface', sig. civ.   [3] Ibid., sig. A^{iii}r.

[4] Ibid., sig. biiir; sig. diir.

[5] Ibid., sig. A^{iiii}r. See Paul Kristeller, *Renaissance Thought* (New York, 1961), pp. 48–69.

[6] Ibid., sig. liiv.

[7] F. R. Johnson, 'The influence of Thomas Digges on the progress of modern astronomy in Sixteenth Century England', *Osiris* I (1936) 390–414.

Aristotle', Digges exclaimed.[1] Following Copernicus, it was in terms of Aristotelian concepts that Digges chose to express his views.

No discussion of the scientific milieu of Elizabethan and early Jacobean England can lay claim to adequacy without some mention of William Gilbert. It is, by now, a cliché to hail Gilbert as one of the first experimental scientists, but there is much truth in this well-worn example. Gilbert's preface to the *De Magnete* can stand as a battle-cry for seventeenth-century scientists. '[I]n the discovery of secret things and in the investigation of hidden causes, stronger reasons are obtained from sure experiments and demonstrated arguments, than from probable conjectures and the opinions of philosophical speculators. . . .'[2] What differentiates Gilbert from Dee is this: Gilbert in his classic work on the loadstone far more clearly exhibited what he meant by experimental knowledge than did Dee. It must be stressed, however, that Gilbert, too, was firmly rooted to the past. Although his 'magnetick philosophy' later gave great impetus to the new mechanical philosophy, Gilbert cannot be deemed a forerunner of the future mechanical philosophers. His analysis still retained the Aristotelian categories of form and matter,[3] and he utilized them in a decidedly scholastic way.[4] Like most innovators, Gilbert's links with the past are quite apparent.

Whereas Gilbert, Digges, and Dee were all in some sense 'Aristotelians', this appellation cannot be applied at all to Giordano Bruno. Bruno belongs in our discussion of this English scientific milieu by virtue of his short stay at Oxford and London (1583–5) during which time he published five very important works.[5] These books were widely read, or at least were read by Percy and the members of his circle. As is well known, Bruno was a Copernican of a 'radical' sort, subscribing to the Democritean doctrine of an infinite universe, with an infinity of (Copernican) worlds. But another truly important aspect of his thought must not be overlooked. Bruno was an atomist, and as such rejected the entire Aristotelian framework of explanation. It is true that Dee and Digges undermined later scholasticism by rejecting the 'infallibility' of Aristotle (if indeed this ever existed) and (in the case of Digges) by exposing his weakness in the area of astronomy. Bruno, however, by espousing what Englishmen may have taken for Epicurean atomism, opened the way for an entirely new natural philosophy. Combining Platonic-Pythagorean emphasis upon mathematics, with a

[1] Thomas Digges, 'Perfit Description of the Coelestiall Orbes', ed. F. R. Johnson, *Huntington Library Bulletin* No. 5, (1934) 80.

[2] William Gilbert, *On the Loadstone,* trans. P. Fleury Mottelay, (n.p., 1892), p. xlvii.

[3] Ibid., p. 85. See also W. J. King, *Natural Philosophy of William Gilbert and his Predecessors* (Washington, 1959), *passim*.

[4] Gilbert's *De Mundo* was, however, directed against the Peripatetics.

[5] *Cena de la Ceneri, De la Causa principio e Uno, De l'Infinito Universo e Mondi, De gli Eroici Furori, De le Bestia Trionfante.*

neo-Epicurean doctrine of atomism, Bruno provided a fruitful new mode of explanation which Percy, Hariot, Hill, Warner, *et al.* were prepared to explore.[1]

Bruno's atomism received its fullest exposition in his *De triplici minimo et mensura,* first published in Frankfurt in 1591.[2] The work is a chaotic and difficult presentation, in verse form, of this ideas concerning the existence of the minimum in nature and in mathematics. The *minimum,* according to Bruno, is the basis of all things; it has a threefold nature: metaphysical, geometric, and physical. In metaphysics, Bruno was primarily concerned to establish the underlying unity of all nature in God. Thus, he saw in his minimum or monad the substance of *ens* of all things, indeed, too, the principle or germ of all existence,[3] for it is the monad from which all development commences. As a metaphysical entity, the monad serves a double function. First, it is the matrix of reality, the basis for unity, and secondly, it is the substance of the soul. In the minimum is Spirit or God. Through the agency of the monad, God is the source of all energy and change. God is the monad of monads—'*totum, infinitum, verum, omne, bonum, unum*'.[4]

Of more interest to scientifically minded Englishmen of the late sixteenth century was Bruno's doctrine of geometrical and physical minima. The starting point for Bruno's atomism was this: the simplest unit must be the criterion for the quantitative rendering of the complex. The minimum is the source of all measurement, and measurement is the key to all knowledge. All quantitative procedures depend entirely upon the prior definition of the least measure.[5] The extension of these views—expressed earlier by Nicholas of Cusa and to be found (in part) in the account of Epicurus in Diogenes Laertius—to mathematics and the structure of matter makes necessary the existence of indivisibles.[6] How can one say that there exist greater and lesser parts, when one has not defined the least part?[7] The natural philosopher who does not comprehend that the maximum and minimum exist by virtue of the same relation is lacking a precise standard.[8] The basis for all error in physics and in mathematics is the infinite division of the continuum, i.e. ignorance of or refusal to acknowledge the minimum. '*Principium et*

---

[1] It is known that Percy and Hariot read Bruno's work; the extent of Bruno's influence can only be determined by a more thorough examination of Hariot's manuscripts than has been possible thus far.

[2] Giordano Bruno, *Opera Latina,* ed. F. Tocco and H. Vitelli (Florence, 1889), Vol. I, pt. III, 119–361. Henceforth cited as *Opera.*

[3] Bruno, *Opera,* vol. I, pt. III, 138. See also Xenia Atanassievitch, *La doctrine métaphysique et géometrique de Bruno* (Paris, 1923), p. 28. Henceforth cited as Atanassievitch.

[4] Bruno, *Opera,* vol. I, pt. III, 144.

[5] Ibid., vol. I, pt. III, 98.

[6] See Nicholas of Cusa, *The Idiot* (London, 1651), p. 6, and Diogenes Laertius, *Lives of Eminent Philosophers,* trans. R. D. Hicks (London, 1925), II, 589.

[7] Atanassievitch, p. 46.

[8] Bruno, *Opera,* vol. I, pt. III, 158–9; see Atanassievitch, p. 44.

*fundamentam errorum omnium, tum in physica tum in mathesi, est resolutio continui
in infinitum.*[1] The object of analysis, therefore, is to refute Aristotle's proofs
concerning infinite divisibility.

Finite matter, Bruno wrote, cannot be composed of infinite parts. By
subtraction or division of a finite magnitude one reaches a monad or least
part.[2] The fallacy in Aristotle's 'proofs' regarding indivisibility is his
failure to distinguish between minima and their limits (*termini*). According
to Aristotle, since points have no parts, they must touch one another, and
in touching, coincide. Consequently, a line cannot be composed of points.
Bruno countered Aristotle in the following manner. No two minima
(physical or mathematical) are actually in contact except through their
termini. The limit is in 'contact' with several other limits, i.e. minima
'share' their termini.

Variability in nature is due to the composition and recomposition of
minima or physical atoms. Atoms excepted, everything is in a state of
constant change. The flux of atoms persists because the World-Spirit
moves them; the World-Spirit is everywhere and thus nothing is at rest.[3]
Nothing is full, except atoms; nothing is void except those spaces interspersed between atoms. There can be no simple, extended void apart from
the notion of atomicity.[4]

Bruno's position can be summed up in this manner: the key to natural
phenomena and mathematics lies with the notion of the minimum or atom.
It was this concept, as well as his more famous notion of the infinity of
worlds, which impressed itself upon the Northumberland Circle.

Dee, Digges, Gilbert, and Bruno represent, for the purposes of our study,
new currents in natural philosophy in England: Copernicanism, Platonism-
Pythagoreanism, a new emphasis upon experiment, and atomism. All these
doctrines were represented in the Northumberland Circle, though, as was
mentioned above, it is only with great difficulty that the scientific thought
of the members of this group can be reconstructed.[5] For Thomas Hariot,
the task is a bit easier; letters and manuscripts left by him and by Torporley
demonstrate quite clearly that he was a Copernican and an Epicurean
atomist.[6] Moreover, it can be shown that he followed Bruno's dictum and
sought the key to all explanation, mathematical as well as physical, in
atomism.[7] A more extensive treatment of Hariot will be found in Chapter
III. Hariot was the intellectual leader in the Circle, although not all of his
doctrines were accepted *in toto* by all members; other evidence must be

[1] Bruno, *Opera,* vol. I, pt. III, 153.   [2] Atanassievitch, p. 41.
[3] Ibid., p. 73.   [4] Ibid., pp. 73–74.
[5] See above, p. 11.
[6] B.M. Birch MSS. 4458, ff. 6–8; B.M. Add. MSS. 6782, fol. 374.
[7] Ibid., ff. 6–8.

presented to give some idea of the intellectual milieu of the Northumberland Circle.

Henry Percy's primary interests were astronomy, optics, alchemy, and medicine. Accounts of his library and of his books with his annotations reveal these interests quite clearly.[1] He owned, for example, Bruno's *De Specierum Scrutinio et Lampade Combuctorie Raymundi Lulli* (Prague, 1588).[2] He possessed also many books by (among others) Napier, Gilbert, Kepler, Tycho Brahe, Paracelsus, Bruno, della Porta, and Alhazen.[3] The books are primarily in English, Latin, and Italian; the earl retained an Italian reader to aid him.[4] His library was considered extensive for the day. After 1590 he seldom left London; the difficulty in moving his books and chemical equipment (without which he did not travel) rooted him to his home near Charing Cross.[5]

Percy's interests are best reflected in a poem dedicated to him by the famous George Peele:

> Renowned lord, Northumberland's fair flower,
> The Muses' love, patron, and favourite,
> That artisans and scholars dost embrace,
> And clothest Mathesis in rich ornaments;
> That admirable mathematic skill,
> Familiar with the stars and zodiac,
> To whom the heaven lies open as her book
> By whose direction undeceivable,
> Leaving our Schoolmen's vulgar trodden paths,
> And following the ancient revered steps
> Of Trismegistus and Pythagoras,
> Through uncouth ways and unaccessible
> Dost pass into the spacious pleasant fields
> Of divine science and philosophy.[6]

Peele's poem is remarkably accurate; at least, it coincides with other evidence about Percy. First, Percy rejected Aristotelianism ('Leaving our Schoolmen's vulgar trodden paths') and concentrated upon astronomy, mathematics (Pythagoras), and alchemy (Trismegistus). Percy's two

---

[1] See John Shirley, 'Scientific Experiments of Sir Walter Ralegh, the Wizard Earl and the Three Magi in the Tower 1603–17', *Ambix* 4 (1949) 52–66. Henceforth cited as 'Tower'; see also Batho, 'Library', pp. 246–61.

[2] Shirley, 'Tower', p. 65.

[3] Batho, 'Library', p. 254.

[4] Eleanor Rosenberg, 'Giacopo Castelvotro: an Italian Publisher in Elizabethan London and his Patrons', *Huntington Library Quarterly* 6 (1943) 119–45.

[5] Gerald Brenan, *History of the House of Percy* (London, 1902), II, 47. Henceforth cited as *History*.

[6] George Peele, 'Honour of the Garter', in *Works*, ed. A. H. Bullen (London, 1888), II, 316–20.

published writings (neither was published in his lifetime) describe his 'liberation' from Aristotelianism. The first, an untitled essay, was printed by Frances Yates as an appendix to her *Study of Love's Labours Lost.*[1] In the essay, which concerns the incompatibility of scholarly pursuits and a mistress, Percy reconstructed a great revelation while reading Alhazen.

Amongest the rest, as a destinie from eternitie prepared to crosse my desires, there lay an owld *Arabian* called *Alhazen,* which with some anger I angrylie removed, it flying open perhapps by reason of a stationers thred uncutt, yet super- stitiouse in my religion that it was the spirit that directed me by hidden and uncon- ceaveable meanes what was good for my almost marking nothing I light upon a place where a figure seemed somewhat more irregular than his fellowes, which caused an awakinge me out of my mark what it imported with more attention.[2]

Percy found in Alhazen what he conceived to be a focus for opposition to scholastic tenets.

[T]here did I behold a demonstration declaring the hight of the aier with no small wonder, because it had eno bene taught me, *Nullum vacuum in rerum natura.* Unchaining my mynd from the former conceites to behold the project of this great promiser, I studied by still interrupted with the worthes of my Mistris which had sealed deeper impression in my memory.[3]

A more enlightening work of Percy, the *Advice to his Son,* has in it certain recommendations concerning education. The recommendations reflect Percy's views of what may be gleaned from formal education, and must not be taken as the limits of his own studies. The section of interest was in fact written about 1595, near the beginning of his relationship with Hariot, and considerably before the most fruitful years of it. Percy suggested to his son several useful disciplines in which young scholars might best be well versed.

The attaining to the Latin is most of use, the Greek but loss of time; other lan- guages are good and profitable, yet to be laid aside until their own and Latin be perfected. . . . Their minds would be wrought toward deeper contemplations as Arithmetic, Geometry, Logic, Grammar Universal, Metaphysics, the Doctrine of Motion of the Optics [*sic*], Astronomy, the Doctrine of Generation and Corrup- tion, Cosmography, the Doctrine *de Anima,* Moral, Politics, Economics, the art Nauticall and Military.[4]

Apart from the inclusion of optics, economics, and military and naval science, and the exclusion of theology, this appears to be nearly the standard

[1] Frances A. Yates, *Study of Love's Labours Lost* (Cambridge, 1936), pp. 208 ff.
[2] Ibid., p. 208.   [3] Ibid., p. 208.   [4] Percy, *Advice,* p. 67.

scholastic curriculum. Percy, however, interpreted this curriculum in a novel manner. For example, he went on to state:

The Doctrine of Motion delivereth elements certainly demonstrative, for all other parts of natural philosophy, as well as speculative, that tendeth to the discovery of natural motions merely, as such that layeth open the structure of all organical engines artificial, whether they be by weight, springs, fire, air, wind, water, vacuity, rariety, density, upon what grounds soever they be caused or for what use soever invented, either civil, nautical, or military.[1]

Similarly, when Percy wrote of 'the doctrine of generation and corruption' he meant something essentially un-Aristotelian. For Percy, the study of 'generation and corruption' was the investigation of combinations of the invisible corpuscles which compose a body. All the 'accidents' and qualities of matter arise from the action of its atoms.

The Doctrine of Generation and Corruption unfoldeth to our understanding the method general of all atomical combinations possible in homogeneal substances, together with the ways possible of generating of the same substance, as by semination, vegetation . . . etc. with all the accidents and qualities rising from those generated substances, as hardness, softness, heaviness, lightness, tenacity, frangibility, fusibility, ductibility, sound, colour, taste, smell, etc. the application of which doctrine satisfieth the mind in the generation and corruption . . . which part of philosophy the practice of Alchemy does much further, and in itself is incredibly enlarged, being a mere mechanical broiling without this philosophical project.[2]

Percy fused a practical interest in alchemy with an atomistic theory.

Another reflection of the interests of Percy and his circle can be found in that imperfect mirror, Nicholas Hill.[3] Hill was loosely associated with the Northumberland Circle through the patronage of the earl, and the friendship of Ralegh.[4] Today Hill is chiefly remembered through Ben Jonson's lines in which he spoke of

> . . . [A]ll those atomi ridiculous.
> Whereof old Democrite and Hill Nicholas
> One said, the other swore, the world consists.[5]

---

[1] Percy, *Advice,* p. 69.   [2] Ibid., p. 70.
[3] Hill was born in London, around 1570. Educated at the Merchant Taylors' School, he went on to St. John's College (Oxford). His patrons included the Earls of Oxford and Northumberland. After being implicated in a plot involving a natural son of Edward IV, he fled abroad. He died approximately 1610.
[4] Wood, II, pp. 86–87. See also John Aubrey, *Brief Lives,* ed. Andrew Clark (Oxford, 1898), I, 319–20. Henceforth cited as *Lives.*
[5] Ben Jonson, *Works,* ed. W. Gifford and F. Cunningham (London, 1875), VIII, 237.

Of all the members of the Northumberland Circle, Hill was probably the least able and the least original. His *Philosophia Epicurea, Democritiana, Theophrastica propositer simpliciter non edocta* (Paris, 1601) is a confused, self-contradictory *mélange* of the views of many thinkers. Particularly, it is a blend of the thought of the atomists, Aristotle, Nicholas of Cusa, the fabled Hermes Trismegistus, Bruno, Gilbert, and Copernicus.[1] The work is chiefly of interest in that it illuminates the various streams which fed into the group around Percy. Hill, a thinker of minor ability, could only imperfectly reproduce the thought of Hariot, Warner, Percy, and the others.

Despite his scholarly reticence and his lack of interest in religious matters, Henry Percy became vitally associated with the political and religious involvements of his day. His cousin, Thomas Percy, was a leading figure in the Gunpowder Plot, and it was through Thomas that Henry Percy was first suspected, then convicted, of treason to the state.

On 5 November 1605, the Gunpowder Treason of the papists, Guy Fawkes and his fellows, was uncovered. On the previous night, Thomas Percy dined with his cousin, the earl, and may have warned him not to attend the scheduled meeting of Parliament. On 15 November, the Earl of Northumberland was brought before the Privy Council to explain his association with the plotters. The earl argued that the course of his life was unambitious and given to private pleasures. He knew none of the plotters, apart from his kinsman, Thomas.[2] The Privy Council, to which Percy had belonged, was led by his arch-rival, Robert Cecil, and was bolstered by Lord Chief Justice Popham who at Ralegh's trial had called Hariot a 'devil'. Popham suspected the piety of the Northumberland group and would not let the matter rest. Percy was arrested on 27 November and was questioned by Popham about his relations with Ralegh.[3] On 28 November, Coke interrogated Fawkes about Percy, and on the following day Percy himself was questioned. Cecil admitted to the Earl of Dumfermline (the Lord Chancellor of Scotland) on 1 December, that 'The Earl of Northumberland is suspected of having received a general caution from [Thomas] Percy but not of any real knowledge of the real plot.'[4] But the Earl of Northumberland was a rich and powerful lord, and until the plot was himself a member of the Council. Cecil was determined to smash the earl's power, despite the King's disposition towards lenience.[5] Cecil prevailed. Despite the flimsiness of the evidence, the earl was sent to the Star Chamber

---

[1] Nicholas Hill, *Philosophia Epicurea* . . . (Paris, 1601), p. 92.
[2] *Calendar of State Papers Domestic 1603–10* (London, 1857), p. 257. Henceforth cited as *Cal. S. P. Dom. 1603–10.*
[3] Ibid., p. 263.   [4] Ibid., p. 265.
[5] Ibid., p. 295.

in June of 1606.[1] On 27 June he was convicted on several counts.[2] He was fined £30,000 (later reduced to £20,000) and confined to the Tower for life. He remained there sixteen years. Percy took this blow with equanimity. In August 1606, he wrote to his former retainer Dudley Carleton, saying that he could bear his own misfortune but that he regretted the fates of his dependents.[3]

Once in the Tower, Percy proceeded to accommodate himself to his new surroundings. At first he was lodged in the cramped Garden Tower where his father had died in mysterious circumstances. After numerous complaints, he was removed to the more capacious Martin Tower where he was enabled to pursue his scientific and scholarly pursuits.[4] In the Martin Tower, Percy fitted out a separate apartment for Hariot who also visited his friend and former patron, Ralegh. The Wizard Earl kept in the Tower crucibles, retorts, alembics, charts, and globes, and even, it is said, human skeletons.[5] By 1614, the Martin Tower was so crowded with scientific paraphernalia that Percy was obliged to rent the neighbouring Brick Tower from Lord Carew.

Into his prison retreat, Percy drew his scientific retainers—Hariot, Warner, Hues, Torporley, and Allen.[6] The group kept abreast of the latest developments in astronomy, mathematics, physiology, and the physical sciences, and made important contributions in several of these areas. Much of Hariot's physical work, for example, dates from this period. Walter Warner's treatise on the motion of the blood (approximately 1610) reflects the broad interests of the group.[7]

It is impossible to say that the Wizard Earl 'enjoyed' his imprisonment, yet certainly he was able to devote himself to his favourite studies. In 1614 it was reported that

[He] is so well inured to a restrained life that were yt not that the world takes notice that he is in his princes displeasure, he would not seeke to chaunge.[8]

Indeed, when an offer of pardon came in 1617, Percy actually refused it, and preferred to return to the 'three magi' (Warner, Hues, and Hariot) in the Tower.[9] But in 1619 after the deaths of Ralegh and his wife, Dorothy, his outlook began to change. When Hariot died in June 1621, of cancer, the last comfort vanished. The earl accepted his freedom and in 1622 returned

---

[1] John Chamberlain, *Letters*, ed. Norman McClure (Philadelphia, 1939), I, 228. Henceforth cited as *Letters*.

[2] These are listed in Arthur Collins, *Peerage of England, Supplement* (London, 1736), II, p. 734.

[3] *Cal. S. P. Dom. 1603–10*, p. 329. [4] Brenan, *History*, II, 161–2.

[5] Ibid., p. 167. [6] Hill had left for the continent.

[7] See below, Chapter IV, and Shirley, 'Tower', pp. 52–66.

[8] Brenan. *History*, II, 197. [9] Chamberlain, *Letters*, I, 566.

to Petworth. He died there on 5 November 1632, exactly twenty-seven years to the day after the Gunpowder Plot.

As the great patron of a circle of natual philosophers deeply involved with the new science, Henry Percy, the Wizard Earl of Northumberland, in his own right deserves far more attention than has been accorded him. But his place in the history of science has been secured primarily through the efforts of the great (and too little-known) astronomer, mathematician, and physicist, Thomas Hariot, to whom we must now turn.

III

THOMAS HARIOT AND
THE ATOMIC VIEW OF NATURE

A GREAT, deep mine of unexplored scientific material can be found in the manuscripts of Thomas Hariot. Hariot's greatness as a scientist has been obscured by long years of neglect. Today, only a few specialists have begun to glimpse in his work a part of his many-sided genius. The source of this neglect is complicated. Much of it, however, has a simple root: Hariot never published any scientific work within his lifetime, and his manuscripts are in a chaotic, incomplete state. The difficulty in sifting through his papers is enormous; the task has been begun, but the end is not in sight.[1]

Thomas Hariot (1560–1621) was born, raised and educated at Oxford. He entered St. Mary's Hall from which he graduated as Bachelor of Arts on 12 February, 1579. While still an undergraduate, Hariot acquired a reputation as a scientific prodigy, and upon leaving St. Mary's was engaged by Sir Walter Ralegh as mathematical tutor. Ralegh sent him as a surveyor with Sir Richard Grenville's expedition to Virginia in 1585. He returned late the following year to begin work on a book. The slim volume, *A Briefe and True Report of the New Found Land of Virginia,* appeared in 1588. The *Report* was a remarkable work, embodying a commercial and statistical study of the resources of the new colony, and a perceptive social analysis of its natives.

In Virginia, Hariot amazed the Indians with his 'Mathematicall instruments, sea compasses, . . . loadstone, a perspective glasse whereby was shewed manie strange sightes, burning glasses . . . gunnes, bookes, writing and reading, spring clocks that seeme to goe of themselves, and manie other things that wee had'.[2] In turn, Hariot was himself amazed at the natural intelligence and eagerness for learning of the natives. He urged, therefore, kind and lenient treatment 'whereby may bee hoped if means of good government bee used, that they may in short time be brought to civilitie, and the imbracing of true religion'.[3]

---

[1] J. Lohne of Flekkefjord, Norway, has done some admirable research into Hariot's physics. Dr. John Shirley of the University of Delaware is working at present on a facsimile version of Hariot's mathematical papers.

[2] Thomas Hariot, *Briefe and True Report of the New Found Land of Virginia* (London, 1588), sig. E4r.

[3] Ibid., sig. E2v.

Ralegh, a friend and card-playing associate of the Wizard Earl, introduced Hariot to Percy in 1588 or 1589.[1] It was probably through Percy (although the reverse is possible) that Hariot came to know the literati Chapman and Marlowe, and the scientifically-minded Hues, Warner, and Torporley. Hariot was widely admired for the depth and breadth of his learning; his friends reinforced this esteem. Chapman wrote in the preface to *Homer's Iliads*:

Only some one or two places I have shown to my worthy and most learned friend, Master Harriots ... whose judgment and knowledge in all kinds I know to be incomparable and bottomless.[2]

Chapman's poem 'Achilles Shield' was dedicated to Hariot 'to you whose depth of soule measures the height and all dimensions of all workes of weight'.[3] Percy thought so highly of him as to award him a pension; thus was Hariot enabled to carry out his experiments without fear of penury.

Percy leased Sion House near Isleworth from Queen Elizabeth, and was granted it by King James in 1604.[4] It was here that Hariot did his greatest work. His most productive years were from 1590 to 1615; after 1615 his health, which had interfered with his work at least as early as 1606,[5] collapsed entirely. He did little more until his death from cancer in 1621. His work had great range and depth. He was an astronomer of note; his observations with the telescope were made simultaneously with those of Galileo. His contributions to mathematics, the extent of which are still debated, were nevertheless considerable. Finally, as a physicist, Hariot did some of his most exciting, and most neglected, work.

Hariot's reputation as an astronomer (and as physicist and mathematician as well) has suffered from the odd twist of fate which left unfavourable commentators in command of the field. A German, Baron von Zach (1754–1832) attempted to rescue Hariot from obscurity, and was, paradoxically, opposed by the English professors Rigaud and Robertson.[6] Robertson was the first to debate von Zach's laudatory researches on Hariot. Sifting through bundles of Hariot's papers, Robertson came to the absurd

[1] *Biographia Britannica* (London, 1747–66), IV, 2539–43.
[2] George Chapman, *Works*, ed. R. H. Shepherd (London, 1885), III, 4.
[3] George Chapman, *Poems,* ed. Phyllis Bartlett (New York, 1941), p. 31.
[4] De Fonblanque, II, 249.
[5] Hariot to Kepler, 6 Dec. 1606, in Johann Kepler, *Gesammelte Werke,* ed. Max Caspar, W. Von Dyck, and F. Hammer (Munich, 1937–63), XV, 368. Henceforth cited as *Werke.*
[6] J. Lohne, 'Fair Fame of Thomas Harriott', *Centaurus* **8** (1963) 69. Henceforth cited as 'Fame'.

conclusion that they deserved their obscurity for no longer could they 'contribute to the advance of science'.[1] Hariot's work on mechanics (*c.* 1600) was disparaged by comparison with a similar work by John Keill (*c.* 1700). Rigaud's examination of Hariot's astronomical papers was less preposterous, although equally (and inexplicably) hostile. Rigaud's 'mission' as a historian was one of safeguarding the reputation of Galileo from the English interloper. Rigaud did, however, publish a good account of the manuscript material.[2]

Hariot's important observations were made as early as 1609. It is certain that as early as July 1609, he employed a telescope in viewing the moon.[3] Even Rigaud admits that 'It is perfectly clear that Hariot and his friend [Sir William Lower] had been in the habit of using telescopes before the discoveries of Galileo were known to them.[4] Hariot was one of the first systematic observers of sun-spots. On 8 December 1610, he drew a very clear diagram of them. His sightings of 1610 were the first of a series of such observations and are the earliest known extant.[5] Galileo, it should be noted, first published his findings on sun-spots in 1613.[6] Hariot also viewed the moons of Jupiter with his telescope and calculated their periods as his manuscripts clearly show. Like those of sun-spots, his observations of Jupiter's satellites are the earliest known to exist today.[7] The earliest reference is dated 16 January 1610, *ex propris observantis*;[8] a whole series of observations dates from 17 October 1610.[9]

Hariot and his disciples were the first Keplerians in England; they were the first to accept elliptical orbits. On 6 February 1610, William Lower, Hariot's pupil, wrote to him that many of Hariot's 'inventions' were being taken from him because of his failure to publish them. 'I remember long since you told me as much, that the motions of the planets were not perfect circles.'[10] Hariot had speculated earlier that the planetary orbits were near-circles; apparently he did nothing further. Lower's letter does, however, establish Hariot as Kepler's leading champion in England. '[A]boute his theorie', wrote Lower, 'me thinks (although I cannot yet overmaster manie of his particulars) he establisheth soundlie and as you say overthrowes the circular astronomie.'[11] It was not until Jeremiah Horrox in the

---

[1] A. Robertson, 'On Some Mistakes relating to Dr. Bradley's Observations, and Harriot's MSS.'. *Edinburgh Philosophical Journal* 6 (1822) 313–18.

[2] Stephen Rigaud, *Supplement to Bradley's Miscellaneous Works* (London, 1833), *passim.* Henceforth cited as *Supplement.*

[3] Rigaud, *Supplement,* pp. 20, 48.   [4] Ibid., p. 27.

[5] Ibid., plate III, supp.   [6] Ibid., p. 32.

[7] Ibid., p. 37

[8] Rigaud maintains that Hariot calculated this 'observation' from Galileo's observations. Rigaud, *Supplement,* p. 29.

[9] Ibid., plate II, supp.   [10] Ibid., p. 43.

[11] Ibid., p.43.

mid-seventeenth century that another English astronomer adopted Kepler's laws.[1]

It is interesting to note that Lower was the first to suggest elliptical orbits for comets. Lower pondered 'his [Kepler's] elliptical *inter planetarum* for me thinkes it shewes a way to the solving of the unknown walkes of comets.'[2]

Hariot's mathematical reputation rests (unfortunately) solely upon his *Artis analyticae praxis*, published posthumously from his fragmentary notes by his students, Walter Warner and Sir Thomas Aylesbury. The *Praxis* does not represent Hariot's best or most important mathematical work. It doubtlessly would have been much improved had Hariot himself compiled and edited it.

The first expositor of Hariot's algebra was John Wallis.[3] In his *Treatise of Algebra*, Wallis supplied an exhaustive list of Hariot's algebraic innovations.[4] Wallis was also a major source of another widespread notion: that Descartes plagiarized from Hariot. According to Sir Charles Cavendish, Dr. John Pell and the French polymath Roberval, Descartes plagiarized Hariot's device of putting the entire equation on one side of the equality, letting it equal zero.[5]

Wallis was doubtlessly too exuberant in his praise of Hariot. But in the reaction against Wallis, Florian Cajori[6] committed the opposite error. Cajori credited Hariot with (1) introducing 'canonical equations', (2) employing the signs $<$ and $>$, (3) placing the equation on one side of the equality, and (4) improving numerical approximation.[7] But, said Cajori, he did *not* show that an nth degree equation has n roots, except in the case $(a-b)(a-c)(a-d)=0$, because Hariot, with one exception, did not admit negative roots. This single instance presented Cajori with some difficulty. 'From Hariot's sentence', he wrote, 'we may infer that he recognized the possibility and considered the advisability of admitting into his algebraic system negative roots of equations, but that he decided such a course would be quite useless.'[8] J. F. Scott devotes a long (and excellent) section of his *Mathematical Work of John Wallis*[9] to refute many of Wallis' claims.

Both Cajori and Scott worked primarily from the *Praxis* although Scott did look at some of Hariot's manuscripts. In the manuscripts, however,

[1] I am indebted to Mr. Wilbur Applebaum of the University of Illinois for first pointing out to me the extent and importance of Hariot's Keplerianism.
[2] Rigaud, *Supplement*, p. 43.
[3] John Wallis, *Treatise of Algebra* (London, 1685).
[4] Ibid., pp. 199–200.   [5] Ibid., p. 198.
[6] Florian Cajori, 'A reevaluation of Harriot's *Artis Analyticae Praxis*', Isis **11** (1928) 316–24.
[7] Ibid., pp. 323–4.   [8] Cajori, p. 320.
[9] J. F. Scott, *Mathematical Work of John Wallis* (London, 1938), pp. 134–62.

some of Wallis' claims are vindicated, and even new claims for Hariot can be made. Hariot *did* employ negative roots,[1] although from his standpoint, which was primarily that of a physicist, they were often to be neglected. For a long period of time, Hariot was interested in problems of free fall and of fall in resistant media; he found negative roots less useful in solving these problems.

Hariot did have a rudimentary analytic geometry as F. V. Morley claimed,[2] i.e. Hariot utilized the equivalence of equations and geometric figures.[3] Many other mathematical triumphs can be laid at Hariot's door. In 1603, Hariot discovered a method of computing the area of the spherical triangle which had been sought since antiquity.[4] He also made important advances in interpolation which were later studied by Sir Charles Cavendish and Dr. John Pell.[5] Morley reported that he had seen in Hariot's manuscripts a 'well-formed analytical geometry with rectangular co-ordinates and recognition of the equivalence of equations and curves, and notes on tables of binomial coefficients worked out in Pascal's triangle and Fermat's square'.[6] Finally, Hariot was one of the first to employ binary numeration. John Shirley has shown that Hariot had experimented with binary numbers and higher order systems (ternary, quaternary, etc.) as well.[7]

Having seen no practical application of these systems, Hariot soon lost interest in them. His point of view was that of a physicist and natural philosopher. He was interested in mathematics in so far as it would be of use in his physical researches. His physical and astronomical studies were, in turn, merely stepping-stones toward a more complete understanding of the secrets of nature. Hariot saw himself as his admirers saw him: possessed of a new method for plumbing the depths of nature's mysteries. This method was 'experimental' in a very modern sense. His amazingly original work in physics bears witness to his genius.

Hariot's major area of interest was physical optics. His work is an excellent example of experimental science in the early seventeenth century, before Bacon's *Novum Organum*. John Shirley has described a report of Hariot's disciples Warner and Aylesbury to the mathematician John Pell, in which they claimed priority for Hariot in the discovery of the law of refraction. Pell reported:

Mr. Warner says he had of Mr. Hariot this proportion as the sine of one angle of incidence to the sine of its refracted angle, found by experience, so the sine of any

[1] Rigaud, *Supplement,* plate V, supp.
[2] F. V. Morley, 'Thomas Hariot', *Scientific Monthly* **14** (1922) 60–66.
[3] B.M. Add. MSS. 6784 ff. 1–41.   [4] Lohne, 'Fame', p. 79.
[5] Ibid., p. 81.   [6] Morley, p. 64.
[7] John Shirley, 'Binary Numeration before Leibniz', *Am. J. Phys.* **19** (1951) 452–4.

angle of incidence upon the same superficies to the sine of the refracted angle to be found by supputation.[1]

Warner verified Hariot's law of refraction and the apparatus employed, surprisingly modern, was fully described.[2] Shirley wrote that Hariot's actual manuscript notes of his experiments 'do not appear to exist'.[3] Lohne has shown that (1) Hariot found the sine law of refraction after several years of systematic search in 1601,[4] (2) using a prism, he measured the dispersion of white light,[5] (3) he was the first to solve the problem of the radius of the rainbow,[6] and (4) he found in 1605 that green and red rays have different refrangibilities.[7] Hariot promised a full treatment of the problem of colour; this work has not been found.[8]

These optical discoveries alone would be enough to establish Hariot as the peer of Galileo and one of the greatest English scientists before Newton.[9] But he also made interesting and original researches in mechanics which deserve further study.

In a letter of 1610, Lower reminded Hariot that '[Y]ou taught me the various ways to observe weight in water, and within a while after Ghetaldi comes out with it in print.'[10] Indeed Hariot made extensive, accurate measurements on specific gravities. His tables were very much better than those of Ghetaldi's *Archimedes Promotus* of 1603.[11] Hariot's manuscripts contain drawings of a hydrostatic balance which he invented in 1604.[12] He was also interested in hydrodynamics, as for example the flow of water in pipes, and the general properties of motion in a resistant fluid. 'Bodies moving in a medium', he wrote, 'do affect to carry a pyramid of the same medium [in front] but the top is broken off'.[13]

Lohne has done interesting research on Hariot's contributions to the

[1] B.M. Add. MSS. 4407, fol. 183, quoted in John Shirley, 'An Early Experimental Determination of Snell's Law', *Am. J. Phys.* **19** (1951) 507.
[2] Ibid., p. 508.
[3] Ibid., p. 507.
[4] Lohne, 'Thomas Harriott, the Tycho Brahe of Optics', *Centaurus* **6** (1959) 166. Henceforth cited as 'Optics'.
[5] Ibid., p. 119. See B.M. Add. MSS. 6789, fol. 198. Henceforth cited as 'Optics'.
[6] Ibid., p. 118.
[7] Lohne, 'Fame', p. 83.
[8] Hariot to Kepler, in Kepler, *Werke,* XV, 368.
[9] Lohne's complete account of Hariot's optical discoveries is expected to appear in the *Acta Historica Scientiarum Naturalum et Medicinalum.*
[10] Rigaud, *Supplement,* p. 43.
[11] Lohne, 'Fame', p. 80. Hariot's tables should be compared with those of Francois de Foix, among others, before any definite statement concerning their originality is made.
[12] B.M. Add. MSS. 6788, fol. 231; see also R. T. Gunther, *Early Science in Oxford* (Oxford, 1923), I, 239.
[13] B.M. Add. MSS. 6788, fol. 145; see Gunther, I, p. 208.

theory of projectiles resisting media.[1] According to Lohne, Hariot proceeded from the medieval mathematician Heytesbury's assumption of
uniformly accelerated motion. He considered the air resistance by assuming
a parabolic path with an oblique axis. Through actual experiment, Lohne
maintains, he measured the gravitational acceleration within the limits
$21 < g < 32\frac{1}{2}$ ft/sec². This work (if corroborated) demonstrates an amaz-
ing sophistication both theoretical and experimental on Hariot's part.

Hariot was also very interested in the motion of falling bodies. Among
his manuscripts is an interesting examination of the fall 'downward from
any poynt aloft naturall and free'.[2] The document is very difficult to assess.
It is fragmentary, and parts of it are illegible. The manuscript suggests that
Hariot may have arrived at the notions that the distance fallen by a body is
proportional to the square of the velocity attained and that the distance is
likewise proportional to the square of the time elapsed. If this suggestion is
correct, Hariot apparently glimpsed these laws some three decades before
Galileo's classic work. A fuller discussion of this difficult document is not
suitable here; the interested reader is referred to the original manuscript,
and to Lohne's papers concerning Hariot's mechanics.[3]

Underlying Hariot's researches in physics was a complete and well-
thought natural philosophy. Like many of the great seventeenth-century
physicists, Hariot was an atomist. Explaining to Kepler the secrets of
physical optics, he wrote:

I have now led you to the doors of nature's house, wherein lie its mysteries. If
you cannot enter because the doors are too narrow, then abstract and contract
yourself into an atom, and you will enter easily. And when you later come out
again, tell me what wonders you saw.[4]

Hariot followed his own advice. In order to penetrate nature's secrets, he
adopted the atomic philosophy in mathematics and in physics. The sources
of his atomism are obscure. Doubtlessly, he was familiar with the atomism
of Giordano Bruno, Hero of Alexandria, Lucretius, and through Diogenes
Laertius, Democritus, and Epicurus.[5]

The question of atomism revolved, for Hariot, around the two infinities.
Aristotle had maintained that while the universe itself was finite, the matter
of which it was composed was indefinitely divisible. Democritus and Epicurus took an opposite view. While the universe was infinite, they claimed,

[1] B.M. Add. MSS. 6789; *Br. J. Hist. Sci.* **1** (1962) 185; 'Ballistik og bevegelseslaere
pa Galileis tid', *Fra Fys. Verd.* No. 1 (1964) 1–4.
[2] B.M. Add. MSS. 6789, fol. 62.
[3] B.M. Add. MSS. 6789, fol. 62; Lohne, op. cit.
[4] Hariot to Kepler, in Kepler, *Werke*, XV, 368.
[5] De Fonblanque, II, 629, shows Percy had works of Hero in his library, as well as
those of Bruno.

the matter of which it was composed was divisible only to a basic indivisible —the atom. Hariot adopted the view of the Epicureans. Everything in nature could be resolved into indivisibles. Yet certain problems remained. How can infinities be composed of finites? How are finites composed of indivisibles in view of the paradoxes which then arise? Is there a transition from the finite to the infinite through a maximum finite? In his manuscript entitled 'De infinitis', Hariot attempted to solve these problems by adopting the notion of the mathematical indivisible.

Out of the finite is generated the infinite. The infinite is composed of the finite. The finite is resolvable into indivisibles. The finite is composed of indivisibles.[1]

He attacked the problem through an analysis of infinite series. 'And yet for a last in decreasing progressions we must needs understand a quantitie absolutelie indivisible; but multiplicable infinitelie infinite till a quantitie absolutelie unmultiplicable be produced which I may call universally infinite . . . And in increasing progressions we must understand that for a last there must be a quantity unmultiplicable absolutelie but divisible infinitelie infinite till that quantity be issued that is absolutelie indivisible'. Thus, he concluded that infinites are generated from finite indivisibles or mathematical 'atoms'.

According to Hariot, the universally infinite quantity generated from mathematical atoms, and the atoms themselves have actual or real existence, as opposed to mere suppositional or 'mental' being. They have 'not onelie act rationall by supposition: but also act reall or existence . . . with many reall consequences or properties consequent'.[2] This confidence in the existence of mathematical-physical indivisibles was the foundation of Hariot's natural philosophy. Moreover, Hariot went on to maintain that all mathematical lines are composed of atoms. In particular, the examined the problem of the construction of a circle from such atoms. The periphery of a circle must be composed of an infinite number of atoms, or else it would not be possible to draw an infinite number of lines from the centre to the circumference. 'Every line is composed *ex atomis*, therefore, on the peripherie of a circle one *atomus* is succeeding one an other infinitelie in such manner as that the peripherie is at last compunded and made.'[3] The number of atoms in the area of the circle must also be infinite, although not necessarily the same order of infinity. Galileo later reached similar conclusions, that is, that lines and surfaces are composed of an infinity of atoms.[4]

[1] B.M. Add. MSS. 6785, fol. 436.   [2] B.M. Add. MSS. 6782, fol. 363.
[3] B.M. Add. MSS. 6782, ff. 369–73.
[4] Galileo, *Dialogues concerning Two New Sciences,* trans. H. Crew and A. de Salvio (New York, 1914), p. 25.

Investigating mathematical indivisibles, Hariot was in actuality concerned with the properties of material bodies.[1] All his reasoning centred around a physical theory of matter. Nature, he held was constructed of eternal and indestructible atoms. Hariot's philosophy focused upon the motion of these material particles.

Hariot's theory of matter appears to have been virtually that of Democritus, Hero of Alexandria, and, in large measure, that of Epicurus and Lucretius. According to Hariot the universe is composed of atoms with void space interposed. The atoms themselves are eternal and continuous. Physical qualities result from the magnitude, shape, and motion of these atoms, or corpuscles compounded of them.[2] The role of *motion* was central. 'Nothing is done without motion. There is no motion without a cause. Out of nothing comes nothing'.[3] It is likely that Hariot's interest in the laws of falling bodies and impact was related to this central role of motion in his natural philosophy.

Homogeneous bodies were thought by Hariot to have atoms of similar shape and in similar density. The denser bodies consist of atoms touching on all sides, whereas lighter bodies have relatively more void spaces intermixed. Chemical changes in weight are caused by the interposition of smaller atoms into the vacua between larger ones. Brittle and soft bodies differ primarily in the magnitude and shape of the component particles.

Probably the most interesting application of Hariot's atomic theory was in the field of optics. In a letter to Kepler on 2 December 1606, Hariot outlined his views.[4] Why, he asked, when a light ray falls upon the surface of a transparent medium, is it partially reflected and partially refracted? Since by the principle of uniformity, a single point cannot both reflect and transmit light, the answer must lie in the supposition that the ray is resisted by some points and not others.

A dense diaphanous body, therefore, which to the sense appears to be continuous in all parts, is not actually continuous. But it has corporeal parts which resist the rays, and incorporeal parts vacua which the rays penetrate. So that refraction is nothing else than an internal reflection, and the part of the rays which are received inside, although to the sense it appears straight, is nevertheless composed of many straight line segments.[5]

It was here that Hariot advised Kepler to abstract himself mathematically into an atom in order to enter 'Nature's house'.[6] In his reply of 2 August

[1] B.M. Add. MSS. 6782, fol. 362.
[2] B.M. Birch MSS. 4458, fol. 6; see Jean Jacquot, 'Thomas Harriot's Reputation for Impiety', *Notes Rec. R. Soc. Lond.* 9 (1952) 183–86. Henceforth cited as 'Impiety'.
[3] B.M. Add. MSS. 6788, fol. 493.
[4] Hariot to Kepler, in Kepler, *Werke*, XV. 365–8.
[5] Ibid., 367–8.   [6] Ibid., p. 368.

1607, Kepler declined to follow Hariot, *ad atomos et vacua*.[1] Kepler preferred to think of the reflection-refraction problem in terms of the union of two opposing qualities—transparence and opacity. Hariot was surprised. 'If those assumptions and reasons satisfy you, I am amazed (*Si illae assumptiones et rationes tibi satisfaciunt, miror.*)' Moreover, 'I confess that my opinion is founded upon the doctrine of a vacuum. . . . But things are such that I cannot as yet freely philosophize.'[2] He added, 'in order not to leave a vacuum on this page', that gold is very dense and opaque, yet gold leaf is translucent.[3]

The importance of atomism in Hariot's thought must be clearly recognized. Whereas Kepler, for instance, clung to Aristotelian modes of scientific explanation, Hariot liberated himself from the scholasticism in which he was trained, and turned to ancient atomism for his basic principles. For Kepler, the nature of reflection and refraction could be explained in a satisfying manner by invoking two contrary qualities, translucence and opacity. For Hariot, this treatment lacked vigour and clarity. He required what can be termed a *physical* rather than a *verbal* explanation. The basis for his view was the teachings of the ancient pagan philosophers.

In two very real and important senses Hariot's was a *mechanical* philosophy. First, the widespread introduction of mining and other machinery provided both a convenient physical analogy for natural philosophy and an important subject for explanation. Hariot and his friends used the analogy of the machine to explain phenomena, and in turn explained the action of machines by matter and motion in the void. One need only recall the Earl of Northumberland's redefinition of the old category of motion, emphasizing the working principles of machines. Secondly, Hariot and his disciples relied solely upon matter and its motion for physical explanation. It is this unique reliance which marked the mechanical philosophies of the mid-seventeenth century.

Why was Hariot so reluctant to make known his views on atoms and the void? Why was he unable, in his own view, to philosophize freely? Hariot's difficulties in this regard stemmed from a long series of religious and political involvements with the English authorities. In the 1590s, Sir Walter Ralegh and his friends, of whom one of the more famous was Hariot, were under suspicion of atheism. In 1591, Robert Parsons denounced Hariot as an Epicurean atheist and conjuror.

[We shall] have to expect but that at some time or another we shall actually see a proclamation drawn up by that Magus and Epicurus, Raleigh's teacher, and published in the name of the Queen by which every single owne beinge, the

---

[1] Kepler to Hariot, in Kepler, *Werke*, XVI, 32.
[2] Hariot to Kepler, 13 July, 1608, in Kepler, *Werke*, XVI, 172.
[3] Ibid., p. 173.

immortality of every soul, and the expectation of another life, are distinctly, clearly briefly and with circumlocution denied.[1]

Parsons further wrote:

Of Sir Walter Ralegh's school of atheism, by the way, and of the conjuror that is M[aster] thereof, and of the diligence used to get young gentlemen to this school, wherein both Moses and our Savior, the old and the New Tetament are justed at and the scholars taught among other things to spell God backward.[2]

Parsons was supported by Richard Baines who declared that Christopher Marlowe had maintained

[T]hat Moyses was but a Jugler, and that one Heriots, being Sir W. Raleigh's man, can do more than he.[3]

A commission on atheism was called at Cerne Abbas on 21 March 1594, to investigate such charges. The rumours grew wilder and more speculative. One witness declared that he 'hath harde that one Heryott of Sir Walter Raleigh his howse hath brought the godhedd in question, and the whole couse of the scriptures'.[4] Another maintained that he had heard that Hariot denied the 'resurreccion of the bodye'.[5]

Nothing came of the Cerne proceedings. But the stigma of atheism clung to Hariot. At Ralegh's trial, Chief Justice Popham is said to have declared:

Let not Heriott nor any such Doctor, persuade you there is no eternity in Heaven, let you find an eternity of hell-torments.[6]

This reputation for impiety bore evil fruit in 1605. In November of that year, Guy Fawkes and his co-conspirators plotted to blow up the Houses of Parliament. The Earl of Northumberland was arrested, imprisoned, and tried in the Star Chamber for treason.[7] Hariot, too, was suspected. His reputation as a mathematician and astronomer brought with it notoriety as a conjuror and astrological necromancer. The King was particularly anxious. James I asked that Hariot be interrogated about 'casting the king's nativity'.[8] Hariot's student, Nathanael Torporley, was questioned about his astrological activities with Hariot, pertaining to the King and the

---

[1] Quoted in Norman Williams, *Sir Walter Raleigh* (London, 1962), pp. 105–6.
[2] Robert Parsons, *An Advertisement written to a Secretary of My Lord Treasurer of England* (London, 1592), p. 18.
[3] G. B. Harrison, ed., *Willobie His Avisa* (London, 1926), p. 210.
[4] Ibid., p. 258.
[5] Harrison, *Willobie His Avisa*, p. 260.
[6] David Jardine, *Criminal Trials* (London, 1832), I, 450–51.
[7] See above, p. 26.
[8] Historical Manuscripts Commission, *Salisbury Manuscripts* (London, 1938), XVII, 530. Henceforth cited as *Salisbury MSS.*

Prince of Wales.[1] Hariot's rooms at Sion were searched for evidence of disloyalty or unorthodoxy. Sir Thomas Smith reported to Salisbury:

I have made as diligent a search of Mr. Herriott's lodging and study at Sion as the time would permit. To have made an exact survey of all papers there would have required many days, and I think it would not be to any purpose, because it be all of another sort than such as I should find. Letters there are few, almost none, and such as are carry an old date. Books of all sorts of learning and many: of all sorts and professions of religion: but neither one place or other, though I opened all his chests has afforded one anything needful to be brought to you. I have therefore sealed up his study close and his chests to the end there may be a more exact survey if you shall think meet. My Lady of Northumberland, with great respect unto the warrant that I had and with all willingness, yielded to the making of the search.[2]

Despite the lack of any real evidence, Hariot was arrested and imprisoned. The dates and nature of his confinement are unknown, although Hariot was under arrest by December 1605. He wrote twice to effect his release. On 16 December 1605, he wrote to the Privy Council that he was not a meddler in mattres of state, and was contented with a private life 'for the love of learning'. His labours, he wrote, 'have been painful and great'.[3] The 'misery of close imprisonment' at the time of his sickness, will result, he claims, in his death. His desire to continue his studies and regain his health made him 'a suitor for liberty'.[4] This is the first evidence of the long illness which prematurely ended his life and studies. He also wrote to Salisbury in 1605 to beg his release 'out of this dungeon of many miseries'.[5]

It is no wonder, then, that when he finally regained his freedom, he was loath to give full expression to views which would mark him as politically or theologically unorthodox. His atomism, deriving in part as it did from the ancient atheistic materialists Lucretius and Epicurus, was naturally considered suspect. Indeed, he was attacked on this very ground.[6]

According to Aubrey, Hariot's death in 1621 was looked upon by contemporaries as God's retribution.[7]

[H]e did not like (or valued not) the old storie of the Creation of the World. He could not beleeve the old position; he would say *ex nihilo nihil fit*. But . . . a *nihilum* killed him at last: for in the top of his Nose, came a little red speck (exceedingly small) which grew bigger and bigger and at last killed him.[8]

Despite Aubrey's contention that 'He made a philosophicall theologie wherein he cast off the Old Testament, and, the New-one would (consequently) have no foundation. He was a Deist,[9] there is little evidence either

[1] *Cal. S.P. Dom.* (1603–10) (London, 1857), p. 263.
[2] Salisbury MSS. XVIII, 507–8.   [3] Ibid., XVII, 554.
[4] Ibid., XVII, 554.   [5] Ibid., XVII, 600.
[6] See below, p. 59.   [7] Aubrey, *Lives,* II, 287.
[8] Ibid., I, 286.   [9] Ibid., I, 287.

to support or confute Hariot's reputation for impiety.[1] However, the fact that his contemporaries gave credence to the view that he flirted with atheism played an important role in suppression of his atomism.

Hariot published nothing after his *Report* of 1588. He was, nevertheless, not an isolated figure. Through the dissemination of his manuscripts and through his disciples, Hariot's effect upon English science and mathematics was not insignificant. His students included the Earl of Northumberland, Walter Warner, Sir Thomas Aylesbury, Robert Sidney (Lord Lisle), Sir William Lower, and Nathanael Torporley. These men, especially Lower and Warner, deserve far more attention than has been accorded them. The following chapter, in a modest way, will attempt to improve this situation.

[1] For a discussion of Hariot's reputation see Jacquot, 'Impiety', 164–87.

IV
HARIOT'S DISCIPLES

THOMAS Hariot died in 1621. Realizing that his death was approaching, on 9 June of that year he made out his will. In it, he divided his manuscripts among his students, with the expressed wish that they be brought into publishable form.[1] One part, consisting mainly of copies, was awarded to Robert Sidney, Viscount Lisle, and first Earl of Leicester. Sidney was the son-in-law of the Earl of Northumberland, and a close friend and student of Hariot. Another part, after publication by Nathanael Torporley, was to revert to the Earl of Northumberland.[2] It was probably this portion of the manuscripts which came into the hands of Aylesbury and his new secretary and scientific retainer, Walter Warner.[3]

All Hariot's important students with the exception of William Lower— Percy, Torporley, Sidney, Warner, and Aylesbury—came to share in the distribution of his papers. Aylesbury and Warner utilized their share to publish the *Artis analyticae praxis* from Hariot's notes in 1631, an effort roundly criticized by Torporley in his unpublished *Corrector Analyticus*.[4] It was Torporley who Hariot actually hoped would publish his works. Torporley, however, accomplished nothing. Aylesbury and Warner, besides publishing the *Praxis*, were the instruments of Hariot's transmission to the scientific circles of the latter seventeenth century.

Probably the most intriguing of Hariot's pupils was Sir William Lower. Several letters from Lower to Hariot have been preserved, mostly pertaining to astronomy. They show that as early as 1609 or the beginning of 1610 Lower had received telescopes from Hariot, and that there existed at Trafenti in Wales a flourishing school of scientists, 'the Traventane philosophers'. Lower discoursed with Hariot upon several subjects: mathematics, chemistry, physics, and astronomy. In all fields Lower showed himself an apt student.

Lower was born in 1570 of an old and respectable Cornish family. He was educated at Exeter College, Oxford, at which he matriculated in 1586. He remained there until 1593, apparently leaving without a degree. In 1601 he was returned as a Member of Parliament for the last parliament of Queen

[1] Henry Stevens, *Thomas Hariot, the Mathematician, the Philosopher, and the Scholar* (London, 1900), p. 199.

[2] Ibid., pp. 199–201.

[3] Stephen Rigaud, *Correspondence of Scientific Men* (Oxford, 1841), II, 478.

[4] J. O. Halliwell, *Collection of Letters Illustrative of the Progress of Science in England* (London, 1841), pp. 109–16. Henceforth cited as *Collection*.

Elizabeth. He was also returned as a Member of Commons during James' first parliament and remained a Member until 1614. He married Penelope Perrot, the step-daughter of the Earl of Northumberland, and thereby received as dower the estate of Trafenti in Carmarthenshire, in Wales.[1]

Lower's letters to Hariot show that he and a circle of friends were investigating the heavens with telescopes supplied by Hariot as early as the winter of 1609–10.

[T]hes Starres with my Cylinder this last winter [1609–10] I often observed so farre and distinctlie that without I can not yet dissever.[2]

By February 1610, Lower had again received a shipment of telescopes from Hariot, and was observing the moon.[3] Lower was no dilettante astronomer. He apparently had extensive training and was willing to undergo the rigours of untangling the difficult *Astronomia Nova* of Kepler.

But againe to Kepler. I have read him twice over cursoridlie [*sic*]. I read him now with calculation. Sometimes I find a difference of minutes, sometimes false prints, and sometimes an other confusion in his accounts, these difficulties are so manie. . . .[4]

Lower was well instructed by Hariot in mathematics and shared the latter's improvements in algebraic notation. As did Hariot, Lower also dabbled in chemistry. A letter of 19 July 1611, is devoted primarily to chemical questions.[5]

Sir Thomas Aylesbury (1576–1657) was another of Hariot's pupils, self-described as his 'very loyteringe but lovinge skollar'.[6] He too was trained by Hariot in mathematics and astronomy.[7] Aylesbury was born in London in 1576, and educated at the Westminster School and Christ Church, Oxford, where he graduated Bachelor of Arts in 1601 and Master of Arts in 1605.[8] Upon graduation he was appointed secretary to the Lord High Admiral of England, and retained this post when the Duke of Buckingham assumed the position of Admiral in 1618. Aylesbury was a favourite of Buckingham who obtained for him the additional posts of Master of Requests, and Master of the Mint. In 1627 he was created a baronet.

These posts afforded Aylesbury a new affluence. He was able to become a patron of the sciences and maintained his dependents (for example, Walter

[1] Rigaud, *Supplement to Bradley's Miscellaneous Works* (London, 1833), pp. 68–69. Henceforth cited as *Supplement*.
[2] Lower to Hariot, June 1610, in Rigaud, *Supplement,* p. 26.
[3] Lower to Hariot, February 1610, in Rigaud, *Supplement,* p. 42.
[4] Ibid., p. 43.
[5] Halliwell, *Collection,* p. 42.
[6] Aylesbury to Hariot, 15 April, 1613, in Halliwell, p. 43.
[7] B.M. Birch MSS. 4408.
[8] Anthony à Wood, *Fasti Oxonienses* (London, 1833), I, 306.

Warner and Thomas Allen) at Windsor Park and London. In 1642, as a royalist, he was deprived of his fortune, and in 1649, after the beheading of the King, he emigrated to the Netherlands, where he died in 1657 at the advanced age of 81. The Hariot papers in his possession passed to his son-in-law, the famous Earl of Clarendon. Aylesbury, through the marriage of his daughter to Clarendon, became the great-grandfather of two queens —Mary and Anne.[1]

Another notable pupil was Robert Sidney, the Viscount Lisle and first Earl of Leicester. Sidney (1595–1677) was the nephew of the more famous Philip Sidney. After matriculating at Christ Church, Oxford, Sidney served in the military and in parliament before entering Gray's Inn in 1618. In 1616 he married Dorothy Percy, the daughter of the Wizard Earl of Northumberland, and it was probably through his father-in-law that he came to study mathematics with Hariot.

In his will, Hariot chose the Reverend Nathanael Torporley (1564–1632) to edit his manuscripts. This projected edition never was completed, in part because Torporley was out of sympathy with Hariot's religious and philosophical point of view. Torporley was born in Shropshire in 1564. According to Wood,[2] he was educated at Christ Church where he received his Bachelor of Arts in 1584 and Brasenose College, Oxford where he received his Master of Arts in 1591. He entered the ministry and served as Rector of Salwarpe from 1608 to 1622, although he lived chiefly at Sion College (not to be confused with Sion House, Hariot's residence) in London. He died there in 1632, leaving his manuscripts and instruments to the Sion College Library where they now remain.[3] Among his manuscripts is his attack on Hariot's *Artis analyticae praxis* (the *Corrector Analyticus*). The British Museum also possesses an attack upon Hariot's atomism by Torporley.[3]

Torporley joined the Northumberland Circle as a young man and received a yearly stipend from the Wizard Earl. It was during this period that Torporley was tutored in mathematics by Hariot and became his close associate. Torporley soon left for France and spent a year or two as the secretary of the famous French mathematician, François Viète.

Torporley returned to England and remained close to Hariot and his students; Hariot's confidence in him (perhaps misplaced) was such that he named him executor and editor of his mathematical manuscripts. Instead, Torporley chose to call into question the natural philosophy of his mentor.

The defence of philosophy against atomism was promised by Torporley's

[1] Biographical material can be found in the *Biographia Britannica,* as well as the *Dictionary of National Biography*, Wood and Aubrey.
[2] Wood, *Athenae Oxonienses,* II, 524.
[3] B.M. Birch MSS. 4458, ff. 6–8, printed in Jacquot, 'Impiety', pp. 183–7.

earlier *Corrector Analyticus* 'of the posthumous scientific writings of
Thomas Harriot, as an excellent Mathematician one who very seldom erred,
as a bold Philosopher one who occasionally erred, as a frail Man one who
notably erred, for the more trustworthy refutation of the philosophic
atomic theory revived by him'.[1]

Torporley named Hariot as the reviver of the atomic theory, and indeed
the latter was the foremost exponent of it in England. The 'Synopsis',
probably written after 1622, is an extended refutation of Hariot's atomism,
opposing to it the tenets of Aristotle.

First is described the different reasons of Democritus, and Aristotle. . . . Either
Atoms are or bodies are compounded, and resolvable into nihilum. Democritus
abhorring rather than disproving concludeth the first. We disprove demonstratively the first, and so conclude the second, where opposing chiefly T.H.[2]

According to Torporley, the atomic philosophy which maintains the
existence of indivisible corpuscles and space void of matter is patently false.
'There is no vacuum', Torporley held, 'but all space is full'.[3] The starting
point for the refutation of atomism is, therefore, the plenitude of space and
the divisibility of matter. 'Matter', he insisted, 'is divisible'.[4] Since matter
is divisible, any corpuscular unit of matter will be ephemeral rather than
eternal, for by continual division it will lose its form.

The objections to atomism, Torporley held, were too great to be denied,
and he began at once to question the explanation of physical phenomena in
terms of the atomic philosophy. If bodies were truly composed of atoms,
hard and indivisible, then nothing soft could result from their composition.
Again, if as Hariot had held, brittle and malleable bodies differ only in
the magnitude and shape of their respective atoms, how can one explain
the softening of steel merely by adding heat? Similarly, what enables
bodies to change state from fluid to solid and the reverse, as in metals
melted?[5]

Turning to optics, Torporley attacked Hariot's notion that refraction is
merely the repeated reflection of light from the many atoms composing the
refracting medium. Torporley proposed several contrary examples, but the
most telling (from his point of view) was the case of refraction by a coloured
transparent medium, such a coloured glass or gems. Torporley noted that
light *reflected* from the surface of such media is uncoloured, whereas light
transmitted and refracted assumes the colouration of the medium. This
was, indeed, a serious objection; Torporley posed here a difficult problem
for those of Hariot's persuasion.

[1] Stevens, pp. 172–4.
[3] Sion Coll. MSS. ARC 140.2/E10, f. 83 recto.
[4] Ibid.
[2] Jacquot, 'Impiety', p. 183.
[5] B.M. Add. MSS. 4458, f. 6.

Torporley concluded:

Therefore unpossible that there should be Atoms. . . . *Ex nihilo omnia*.[1]

Everything *does* come out of nothing, Torporley defiantly maintained. The dictum of antiquity which Hariot upheld 'out of nothing, come nothing', and its atheistic implications are to his satisfaction refuted. Torporley's friend, Walter Warner, was not so easily convinced.

Walter Warner was perhaps the scientific personality closest to Hariot. Little is known of the life of Warner, save that he was born about 1570, and died around 1642–4. He first appeared on the house lists of the Earl of Northumberland in the 1590s as a retainer probably in charge of the earl's extensive library.[2] He worked closely with Hariot, profited from his genius, and kept alive the memory of his works.

Warner accomplished a great many things of his own. A seventeenth-century rumour credited him with the discovery of the circulation of the blood. Aubrey hints that William Harvey may have learned of the circulation through a friend of Lower and Hariot, William Prothero.

Mr. Warner did tell Dr. Pell that when Dr. Harvey came out with his Circulation of the Blood, he did wonder whence Dr. Harvey had it: but comeing one day to the earle of Leicester he found Dr. Harvey in the hall, talking very familiarly with Mr. Prothero . . . to whom Mr. Warner had discoursed concerning this exercitation of his *De Circulatione Sanguinis* and made no question but Dr. Harvey had his hint from Prothero. Memorandum: Dr. Pell sayth that Mr. Warner rationed demonstratively by beats of the pulse that there must be a circulation of the blood.[3]

Wood also gave support to the rumour.

[Warner] also did make it appear in a Ms. of his composition that the blood in a body did circulate which he communicating to the immortal Harvey, he took his first hint thence concerning the matter which he afterwards published as the first inventor.[4]

Yet a third version can be found in an anonymous manuscript in the Bodleian Library:

Another was Mr. Warrener, the Inventor probably of the circulation of the blood, of which subject he made a treatise consisting of two books which he sent to Dr. Harvey who Epitomized and printed them In his own Name; he usually said that Dr. Harvey did not understand the Motion of the Heart which was a perfect Hydraulick.[5]

---

[1] B.M. Birch MSS. 4458, fol. 8.   [2] Batho, 'Library', p. 248.
[3] Aubrey, *Lives*, II, 291.   [4] Wood, *Athenae Oxonienses*, II, 302.
[5] Quoted in Shirley, 'Tower', p. 55.

Warner published little,[1] but after the fashion of Hariot left voluminous manuscripts which came into the hands of John Pell through Bishop Herbert Thorndike.[2] These papers, particularly the mathematical notes of Warner, were borrowed extensively by John Collins and others who widely discussed them.[3] Warner's mathematical work was perhaps his most durable contribution.

Warner's manuscripts are now to be found among the Pell papers in the British Museum. They include Warner's letter on vision,[4] a reply to it by Robert Payne,[5] and several volumes of mathematical and optical tracts.[6]

Among the Warner manuscripts are many which show that he, like Hariot, was an ardent atomist.[7] It will be useful to investigate Warner's atomism, for it appears to have been a clear, well-thought out natural philosophy, and perhaps can be viewed as a bridge between the earlier Epicurean or Democritean position of Hariot, and the later, more sophisticated corpuscularianism of Hobbes and Descartes.

The starting point for Warner's natural philosophy was a criticism of Aristotle's metaphysical framework, particularly of what Warner called 'Aristotles confused and irresolute doctrine of materia prime [which] hath preiudiced the wits of all his followers that they can frame no certaine conceit at all of it howsoever they seem to utter it in his termes and stile.'[8] In opposition, Warner maintained that the natural world is composed of matter in the form of atoms, *vis* or 'power', and void space or vacuum.

Matter itself can be distinguished by 'corporeity or resistibility (or antitypia or hardness)' which are, in themselves, 'the very quiddity and proper essence of matter.'[9] After all, matter is known only through our sensation of resistibility.[10] The matter of all things in the universe is the

---

[1] Aubrey says (II, 286-7) that the sixth book of Mersenne's *Optics* is Warner's.

[2] Letter, H. Thorndike to Pell, 23 Dec., 1652, in 'Herbert Thorndike, Theological Works', (Oxford, 1844-56), VI, 115-6.

[3] Halliwell, *Collection*, p. 95; Rigaud, *Letters*, II, 175, 180, 218.

[4] B.M. Add. MSS. 4395, ff. 116-18.

[5] B.M. Sloane MSS. 4458, ff. 26-7.   [6] B.M. Harley MSS. 6754-6.

[7] B.M. Add. MSS. 4394-6. The following dicussion is based upon the manuscripts, apparently in Warner's hand, identified as the Warner manuscripts in the British Museum and documents in the same hand among the Pell papers in the British Museum and the Torporley papers at Sion College. The papers can, with reasonable certainty, be ascribed to Warner. The handwriting, the spelling and the language place the documents early in the seventeenth century. Samples of Warner's later handwriting (*c.* 1640) are very similar, but far from identical. Since a paper of similar script, style, and content to those in the British Museum appears in the Torporley collection, and since Torporley died in 1632, I believe we can safely date these documents probably during the 1620's, and certainly before 1632.

[8] B.M. Add. MSS. 4394, f. 396.

[9] B.M. Add. MSS. 4395, ff. 212-3.   [10] B.M. Add. MSS. 4394, f. 386.

same; differences in nature which we experience result from differences in number, shape, magnitude, position, and distance of the bits of matter which compose everything. This prime matter of which all is made exists in the form of atoms, a notion which is demanded by 'the necessary solving of appearances'.[1] Thus, matter consists of finite, discontinuous parts which can neither be created nor destroyed. 'No part of matter', Warner held, 'can perish or be destroied'.[2]

The primal atoms are in motion *'ab aeterno'*.[3] This motion will continue eternally for 'a thing being once in actuall motion howsoever that motion were first impressed or whether it were *ab aeterno* can never alter that state of motion, that is, it can never ... [move] swifter or slower or change forme or way of motion'.[4] Here, in a fragment probably written sometime before 1632, is a clear statement of principle of inertia; this is perhaps one of the earliest of such statements along with those of Hariot and Beeckmann.[5] More specifically, Warner wrote that when a body is moved by some agent, if the agent ceases to act, the body 'doth keep and continue the state of motion without interruption unless it be hindered or stopped by a contrary force and ... what degree of velocity it was at the very instant of the separation of the agent, in the state of the same velocity, it doth continue until the next encounter.'[6] It is not clear from the statement, however, whether motion in a right line only is referred to, or whether other instances are to be admitted.

It is important to note that according to Warner matter is not self-moving, nor apt to move other parts of matter except through transfer of velocity in collision. 'Matter is not moveable *per se* or apt to move itself without the operation of some externall movent.'[7]

Despite the existence of motion *ab aeterno*, some other agent besides body or matter is necessary for the production of 'motions, alternations and effects'.[8] This agent is *vis* or power. Warner is vague regarding the precise nature of *vis*. Of it, he says, that 'All bodies have in them an efficient power or vertue which may be called light whether insensible or sensible.'[9] Or again, 'We must of necessity acknowledge a fourth thing as a cause of motion which may well be termed *vis* or power by the quality of his office whatsoever his substance or quiddity be.'[10] The sole property of

---

[1] B.M. Add. MSS. 4394, f. 383.   [2] Ibid., f. 383.
[3] Ibid., f. 388.   [4] Ibid., f. 388v.
[5] Hariot's formulation (1605 ?) was as follows: 'I say that it is because of the ball's weight that its path bends downward. Without weight it would be along a straight line and if air resistance were removed the ball would continue to move to infinity.' B.M. Add. MSS. 6789; see above, Chapter III, note 50, for Lohne's citation.
[6] B.M. Add. MSS. 4395, ff. 199–200.   [7] Ibid., f. 396v.
[8] B.M. Add. MSS. 4394, f. 389.   [9] Sion Coll. MSS. f. 88v.
[10] B.M. Add. MSS. 4394, f. 389.

vis is the causing of motion; we can attain to little other knowledge about it:

> Seeing therefore that the cheef condition of this *vis* in generall is to cause locall motion (and that of matter, for there is nothing els that can be so much as imagined properly to be moved) it resteth to consider the mover how it is to performe the same and what other conditions it ought to have for the saving of all appearances, the knowledge of which conditions is all the light we possibly can atteyne to of the essence and quiddity thereof and the like is to be understood of matter, time and space.[1]

In short, of the bases of natural philosophy we can know nothing save the conditions of their activity. This credo permitted Warner little flexibility in his discussion of *vis*. One can state, however, with reasonable certainty that Warner thought of *vis* as an immaterial 'power' which, as opposed to dull matter, is interpenetrable and moves *per accidens* rather than moving locally.[2] Moreover, it is reasonably certain that Warner identified *vis* with light, although he did not restrict the latter term merely to visible light.

Both matter and *vis* act within a framework of space and time. According to Warner, both time and space are 'more prime than *materia* and *vis*',[3] for 'to say that matter and *vis* have being is to say that matter or *vis* are contayned in space.'[4] Space itself is 'continueal, eternal, infinite, unalterable, immoveable, absolutely simple', and homogeneous.[5] Space is described as 'an infinit eternall nothing, but the universall vessell or receptacle of thinges'.[6] Time, too, is neither active nor passive and is completely without efficacy.

Matter and 'power' or *vis*, acting in space and time, account for phenomena through *motion*, for 'there is no alteration without motion.'[7] In general, if anything in nature is effected, there must be some cause of that effect; if after the effect is begun the cause ceases, the effect will continue, whether (as in local motion) the state be rest or movement. It is perhaps worthwhile to quote Warner *in extenso* on this point:

> There is no mutation without a cause, that is to say, yf a thing that first had no [being] . . . (or be supposed) afterwards to have being, there is . . . a cause of that mutation from not being to being. And the like yf from being a thing be changed to no being that mutation or change is not . . . without a cause. For like sort, yf a thing that first was in quiet be afterwards moved, there is a cause of that difference or change from quiet to motion, and in the contrary case from motion to quiet, there is likewise a cause. Thirdly yf a thing be first moved in one sort

[1] B.M. Add. MSS. 4394, f. 389   [2] B.M. Add. MSS. 4425, f. 4r.
[3] B.M. Add. MSS. 4394, f. 400.   [4] Ibid., f. 401.
[5] B.M. Add. MSS. 4395, ff. 269–304.   [6] Ibid., ff. 269–304.
[7] B.M. Add. MSS. 4394, f. 382

afterwards be . . . moved in another sort there is a cause of that diversity or alteration of the sort or manner of motion, though the motion in generall be without interruption.[1]

Turning to the origin of variety in natural phenomena, like other atomists Warner held that differences among natural bodies result from differences among their constituent atoms, 'diversity of thinges being indeed nothing els but diverse formes or magnitudes of severall partes or portions of matter ut postea.'[2]

Any two atoms with the same shape or figure, and with equal magnitude, are absolutely identical. They do not differ in what would later be called 'secondary' qualities: colour, odour, taste, hardness, softness, etc. It is only magnitude and shape which cause atoms to differ. There is no colour difference, for instance, because colour is 'nothing but the action of *vis* on the visuall spirits reflected from matter'.[3] In short, gross bodies differ in colour owing to the differences in the superficies from which the *vis* or light is reflected. Weight, too, is a derived quality, being the 'sensation of the *vis* that doth light upon bodies or impell thm which is more or lesse according either to the quantitie of the superficies or solidity of thing impelled'.[4] Likewise, hardness and softness both depend on the 'inward composition and substance of matter'.[5] All these are 'diversified according to the diverse composition and different rarity and density of partes'.[6]

Thus completes the foundation of Walter Warner's natural philosophy. However, Warner did present a qualification to his system in the form of a methodological scholium which demands our attention, for it foreshadows the attitude of the great mechanical philosophers—Hobbes, Gassend, and Descartes—decades later. Although, Warner wrote, there may yet appear some evidence to the contrary we must hold to this system until it is shown deficient.

For all these assais—*a posteriori* drawn from sense there may yet lurk some diversity to us unthought on. . . [but] so longe as we have no meanes to know this but rather finding the contrary, that is simplicity and indifferency to stand and agree with the rest of our Knowledg and the whole course of our theory, and that we finde nothing in the contrary position repugnant to the phenomena but that all appearances may as well or rather better be solved by that position, then by this diversity . . . we are in no sort bound to believe it, but rather the contrary.[7]

In Warner's atomism we can discern subtle changes away from the atomism of Epicurus' *Letter to Herodotus* and perhaps even from that of Warner's

[1] B.M. Add. MSS. 4425, f. 3.   [2] B.M. Add. MSS. 4394, f. 398.
[3] B.M. Add. MSS. 4394, f. 399.   [4] Ibid., f. 399.
[5] Ibid., f. 399.   [6] Ibid., f. 399.
[7] Ibid., f. 399.

4

mentor, Hariot. In Warner there is an increasing concern, even preoccupa-
tion, with fundamental questions. Whereas Hariot appears to have employed atomism as a working, heuristic explanation, a *deus ex machina* to put
order in the chaos of the natural world, Warner appears to have been of a
more systematic posture. Warner's speculations foreshadow the early
mechanistic inquiries of Thomas Hobbes, and the revival of atomism in
more sophisticated form by Pierre Gassend. It is perhaps unwise to draw
too fine a distinction between Warner and Hariot, for Warner may have only
been repeating the teachings of his master; we may never know with
certainty.

Warner's first love was optics, as was Hariot's. It must not be forgotten
that for both Warner and Hariot optics formed an important part of an
entire world-view based upon the atomic philosophy. Warner's interest in
optics was shared, in the 1630s, by an important group of English natural
philosophers with whom he became very close. This group centred around
Thomas Hobbes, Sir Charles Cavendish, and Dr. John Pell.

Thomas Hobbes requires no introduction. His good friend, Sir Charles
Cavendish is unfamiliar to most historians of science. Sir Charles Cavendish
(1591–1654) was the brother of William Cavendish, the Earl, Marquis, and
later Duke of Newcastle, a famous royalist general, poet, and playwright.
Charles served under William at Marston Moor, after which defeat he, like
his brother, went into exile. In 1644 Charles travelled to Hamburg and
Antwerp; in 1645 he joined his brother in Paris. To secure the Cavendish
family estates, he returned in 1651 to England where he died several years
later. His executor, an attorney, died soon after him; the executor's wife, it
is said, sold Cavendish's papers for pasteboard.[1] A mathematician of some
repute and a friend and correspondent of Descartes, Gassend, Mersenne,
Warner, and others, Cavendish was an important (although now forgotten)
figure in scientific circles of the mid-seventeenth century. The loss of the
major part of his papers was indeed a great one for historians of science.

Charles Cavendish was perhaps the first outside Hariot's immediate
circle to become interested in his unpublished manuscripts. It was probably
through Warner that Cavendish learned of the papers. That Cavendish
studied Hariot's works closely cannot be doubted; large portions of the
extant Hariot manuscripts, including more complete versions of *De
infinitis*, are written out in Cavendish's hand.[2]

A friend and colleague of Charles Cavendish was Dr. John Pell, mathematician and divine. Pell was born in Sussex in 1610. He entered Trinity

---

[1] Biographical material for Charles Cavendish can be found in the *Dictionary of
National Biography* (supplement, 1901), *Biographia Britannica,* 2nd ed. (London, 1778), V.
3316, and Lord Clarendon, *Characters of Eminent Men* (London, 1793), pp. 109–10.
[2] Jacquot, 'Impiety', p. 177, n. 37.

College, Cambridge, in 1623, and graduated Bachelor of Arts in 1628 and Master of Arts in 1630. While at Cambridge he acquired great facility in mathematics and in languages, he is reported to have mastered at least ten languages. In 1646, the Prince of Orange invited Pell to teach at the new university of Breda. When war broke out between Holland and England, Pell returned to his homeland in 1652. Despite his royalist connexions, Cromwell sent Pell on a mission to Switzerland. He took holy orders in 1661, and received the doctorate in divinity in 1663. He was elected F.R.S. in that same year.[1]

As a mathematician, Pell was of a minor order; he is best remembered for his invention of the symbol (÷) for division. But to the historian of science and mathematics Pell is an important and interesting figure. He corresponded widely with such men as Hobbes, Petty, Brancker, Hartlib, and Cavendish; he was a friend of Robert Boyle, Walter Warner, Petty, Hobbes, Hartlib, and innumerable other scientific figures. In October 1650, Aylesbury asked Pell to show 'Hariot's doctrine' to a friend; Aylesbury was to supply the original.[2] Pell was eager to receive the papers.

My papers which I have now under hand, tending (I think) to the same ends that those speculations of Mr. Harriots doe. But I speake but by conjecture, I shall be able to say more when I see them.[3]

Through Warner and his papers, Pell became intimately acquainted with the lives of Warner, Aylesbury, and Hariot. It was Pell who was the source for Aubrey's accounts of these men.[4]

During the 1630s, Pell, and Charles Cavendish were members of a small circle of natural philosophers under the patronage of the Earl (later Duke) of Newcastle, William Cavendish. William was born in 1592, the younger brother of the first Earl of Devonshire. In 1620 he was created Viscount Mansfield, Baron Ogle. He was raised to Earl of Newcastle by Charles I and appointed governor of the Prince of Wales in 1638. In 1639 he was chosen leader of the royalist army which he later led to defeat at Marston Moor.[5]

In the 1630s, William Cavendish became interested in science and philosophy and was instructed in these mysteries by Thomas Hobbes. The 'Cavendish Circle' included the two brothers Cavendish, Hobbes, Walter

[1] Biographical material can be found in the *Dictionary of National Biography*; Aubrey's *Brief Lives*.
[2] Helen Hervey, 'Hobbes and Descartes in the Light of the Correspondence between Sir Charles Cavendish and Dr. John Pell'. *Osiris* 10 (1952) 89.
[3] Pell to Cavendish, 14 October, 1651, in Hervey, p. 90.
[4] Aubrey, *Lives*, I, 284.
[5] Biographical sources are the *Dictionary of National Biography*, and the *Biographia Britannica*.

Warner, and Charles Cavendish's secretary, Robert Payne. Warner, whom in optics Hobbes declared to be as able as any man in Europe,[1] became closely associated with the group through Sir Charles and Pell and their interest in Hariot and in optics. As a scientific figure he was much respected by the Cavendishes despite his advanced years, and their sometimes patronizing attitude toward him.[2]

The Cavendish or Newcastle Circle, including Thomas Hobbes, marked a turning point in the fortunes of the atomic philosophy. Hariot and his disciples, who were the first important revivers of the atomic doctrine in England, were for various reasons, *covert* atomists. The Newcastle Circle and those associated with them became the instruments for the open reception of atomism in England as an acceptable natural philosophy. The mechanism of this reception will provide the substance for much of the rest of this history; it involves the giants of the mechanical philosophy— Bacon, Hobbes, Gassend, and Descartes.

[1] Historical Manuscripts Commission, *Portland Manuscripts* (London, 1891), II, 128.
[2] Ibid., p. 131.

V

FRANCIS BACON AND
THE ATOMIC PHILOSOPHY

THE relationship between Francis Bacon, the publicist of the new experimental learning, and the revival of atomism in the seventeenth century has, for several reasons, been clouded in mystery. On the basis of certain very clear statements by Bacon, some have held that he repudiated the atomic view of nature.[1] Others, on the other hand, have looked upon him as the great forebear of the mechanical philosophy,[2] and on the basis of other equally clear statements have made of him an atomic, or rather, a corpuscular philosopher. Both these approaches have a dual failing. In the first place, neither treats Bacon's development as a natural philosopher. Bacon was both an atomist, and an anti-atomist at different points on his long career. The historical evolution of his thought in this respect deserves careful inspection. Secondly, in the rush to see in Bacon the most modern of his contemporaries, his view of matter has been wrenched from its context and distorted to the point of unrecognizability. In his maturity, Bacon was not a mechanical philosopher in the strict sense. To be sure, he did attribute all physical phenomena to the action of matter in motion, but his subtle matter or 'spirit', which was the active agent of phenomena, was endowed with appetition and perception, and interacted with gross matter in ways that the later mechanical philosophers, such as Descartes, would not permit.

In the earliest (Elizabethan) period of his career, Bacon showed little interest in the atomism of Democritus, Epicurus, or Lucretius. But around 1605 his interests appear to have undergone a marked change. The reasons for this change are obscure. It is interesting, however, that it was in these years that Bacon began to have close contacts with the Northumberland Circle. It would be presumptuous to claim that either Hariot or the Earl of Northumberland was in any way the cause of this shift; there does not exist sufficient evidence to decide such a question. Yet, during these years, Bacon declared his awareness of and interest in the scientific work of Northumberland and Hariot, and stated his desire to draw closer to them. It is possible, however remotely, that it was they who quickened his interest

[1] J. R. Partington, 'Origins of the Atomic Theory', *Ann. Sci.* 4 (1930) 262. In his later *History of Chemistry*, II, (London, 1961), he has considerably revised his views.
[2] M. Boas. 'The Establishment of the Mechanical Philosophy', *Osiris* 10 (1952) 439–42. Henceforth cited as 'Establishment'.

in the atoms of Democritus and Epicurus. Writing to the Earl of Northumberland late in 1603, Bacon declared:

[T]here hath been covered in me a long time, a seed of affection and zeal towards your Lordship sown by the estimation of your Lordship. . . . [I]t is very true (and no words or noises in civil matters can blow this out of my head or heart) that your great capacity and love towards studies and contemplations of an higher and worthier nature than popular (a nature rare in this world and in a person of your Lordship's quality almost singular) is to me a great and chief motive to draw my affection and admiration to you. And therefore, good my Lord, if I may be of any use to your Lordship, by my head, tongue, Pen, means or friends, I humbly pray you to hold me to your own.[1]

For whatever help he might offer Northumberland, Bacon clearly expected something in return. His notebooks of 1608 indicate that he looked to Northumberland, to Ralegh, and through them, to Hariot for aid in carrying out his Great Instauration.

The setting on wo. my L. of North. and Ralegh, and therefore Heryott, themselves being already inclined to experiments.[2]

In this period (1603 to 1612 and perhaps later), Bacon showed his greatest sympathy for the atomic doctrine. In the *Cogitationes de Rerum Natura* (written before 1605), in the *De Principiis atque Originibus* (written around 1612), and in the new *Essaies* added in 1612, Bacon made statements most favourable to atomism. They leave no doubt that in this period he was, in some real sense, an adherent of that ancient philosophy.

The doctrine of Democritus concerning atoms is either true or useful for demonstration. For it is not easy either to grasp in thought or to express in works the genuine subtlety of nature, such as it is found in things, without supposing an atom.[3]

At this time the atoms of the ancients, 'unshaken and eternal', were to him a 'necessity plainly inevitable' in natural philosophy.[4] The other pillar of atomism, the void, was also favoured by Bacon.[5] He was later to repudiate both these tenets, i.e. he abandoned the unchangeability of matter and the existence of the vacuum. But in the period under discussion, Bacon found these ideas not only to be true but also useful for the demonstration of religion. Bacon thus became one of the earliest in England to attempt to

---

[1] Francis Bacon, *Life and Letters,* ed. J. Spedding, R. Ellis, and D. Heath (London, 1862), III, 58. Henceforth cited as *Life.*
[2] Ibid., IV, 63.
[3] Francis Bacon, *Works,* ed. R. Ellis, J. Spedding, and D. Heath (Boston, 1861–4), X, 287. Henceforth cited as *Works.*
[4] Bacon, *Works,* X, 387.   [5] Ibid., X, 288–91.

'purify' the atomic doctrine and make it acceptable as a natural philosophy. In his *Essaies* added in 1612 he actually made atomism a support of true religion. According to Bacon, a little learning may lead men away from God, but deeper understanding returns man to Him.

Certainely, a little *Philosophie* inclineth mans minde to *Atheisme,* but depth in Philosophie bringeth man about to Religion. For when the minde of man looketh upon second causes scattered, sometimes it resteth on them; but it flies to providence and *Deitie*.[1]

This phenomenon is well illustrated, he claimed, in the case of the 'atheistic' atomists. The atomic hypothesis, which appears at first glance to be godless, actually reinforces and demonstrates religion:

Most of all, that schools which is most accused of Atheisme doth demonstrate Religion. That is, the school of *Leusippus,* and *Democritus* and *Epicurus*. For it is a thousand times more credible that foure mutable Elements and immutable fifth Essence, duely and eternally placed, needc no God: then that an Army of infinite small portions or seeds implaced should have produced this order; and being without a divine Marshall.[2]

Epicurus, whose 'words are noble and divine',[3] so far from being an enemy of religion was in fact a buttress for it.[4] Democritus, who denied the eternity of the world, but insisted upon the eternity of matter, was closer to 'divine truth' than most others.[5] After all, did not God create the universe out of the pre-existing matter of chaos?

The *Cogitationes de Rerum Natura* (written before 1605) was the first extended atomic treatise of Bacon. The *De Principiis atque Originibus* (*c.* 1612) was an atomic treatise written towards the close of this period. Both were published for the first time in 1653 by Isaac Gruter working from the papers of William Boswell.[6] The *Cogitationes* opens with a definite statement of the truth or utility of the concept of the atom. There are, Bacon maintained, two ways to approach the atomicity of nature. First, the atom can be thought to be the smallest division in nature. Bacon here supported the notion that there is no physical continuum.

[T]here is in things a much more subtle distribution and comminution than falls under view . . . [T]his is not however infinite nor perpetually divisible.[7]

---

[1] Bacon, *Works,* XII, 377–8.   [2] Ibid., XII, 337.
[3] Ibid., XII, 337.
[4] This argument reappeared later in the century in the works of those, such as Walter Charleton, who wished to remove from atomism the taint of atheism.
[5] Bacon, *Works,* XII, 114.
[6] See below, pp. 52–53.   [7] Bacon, *Works,* X, 287.

An 'atom' can also be defined as that particle of matter which admits of no vacuity. Hero of Alexandria was wise, Bacon maintained, to deny the collected void and resort to the interspersed vacuum.[1] However, the opinion of Democritus is to be preferred: a collected vacuity might exist in the region of the air.

But in one respect the conjecture of Hero . . . was inferior to that of Democritus . . .; for Hero because he did not find a collected vacuum in our globe simply denied its existence; whereas there is no reason why in the regions of the air, where there are doubtless greater expansions of bodies, there may not be also a collected vacuum.[2]

As the ancients had insisted, Bacon held that the quantity of matter is fixed, and that all changes in nature occur without loss. 'And as I needed the omnipotence of God to create something out of nothing, so it requires the same omnipotence to reduce something to nothing.'[3] This matter, in the form of atoms, is in constant motion; there is no rest in nature.[4] These atoms, all equal, form groups or corpuscles which are at the source of the alterations found in nature.

The seeds of things, though equal, as soon as they have thrown themselves into certain groups and knots completely assume the nature of dissimilar bodies, till those groups or knots be dissolved.[5]

Bacon's atom is endowed with 'matter, form, dimension, place, resistance, appetite, motion, and emanation'.[6] It is this group of attributes which yield the forms and qualities of gross matter. For instance, fluidity and firmness depend upon the 'appetite of continuity' or mutual attraction of the component atoms.

[I]t is evident that in liquids there is an appetite of continuity, though a weak one; where as on the contrary in solids it is strong and overpowers the natural motion or gravity.[7]

Bacon's theory of matter, in his earlier period, resembles that of Democritus and Epicurus. With respect to *motion*, and the equality of atoms, however, Bacon claimed that the views of Democritus were insufficient. For Bacon, all atoms are identical 'seeds'[8] which act upon each other at a distance; if they did not, no motion could originate and all things would remain fixed and motionless.[9]

---

[1] Bacon, *Works*, X, 288. See also Marie Boas, 'Hero's *Pneumatica*. A Study of its Transmission and Influence'. *Isis* 40 (1949) 47–48.

[2] Bacon, *Works*, X, 290.　　　　　　　　[3] Ibid., X, 298.

[4] Ibid., X, 302.　　　　　　　　　　　　[5] Ibid., X, 292.

[6] Ibid., X, 387.　　　　　　　　　　　　[7] Ibid., X, 302.

[8] Ibid., X, 293.　　　　　　　　　　　　[9] Ibid., XII, 125.

This entire view of the atomic nature of matter was discarded by Bacon, sometime in the period after 1612 and before 1620. By the time of the publication of his *Novum Organum* (1620), he rejected both metaphysical bases of atomism which he had previously accepted: the existence of eternal, immutable atoms and the reality of the void. His previously sympathetic attitude towards Epicureanism was to turn into contempt.[1]

The fall of atomism within Bacon's natural philosophy was caused, it seems likely, by the shaping and sharpening of his *method*. The purpose and content of his *Novum Organum* was diametrically opposed to his former views. Henceforth, the nature of matter was to be determined, in Bacon's works, through the certainty of a new union of *theory* and *practice*. This conception of unity was not new; there were elements of it in the thought of John Dee and of Hariot. But in Bacon, one can find its most complete exposition and application.

Atomism, basically an *a priori* construction, and far removed from 'laboratory' practice, as it were, was sacrificed for a new conception, close to that of the chemists, and to Bacon's mind, more closely related to experience.

In his mature years, Bacon became strikingly aware of the lack of certainty in the intricately woven theories of Greek natural philosophy, which at the beginning of the seventeenth century still held sway. The only course left was to raze the old structure and build anew.[2] Those moderns who rely upon the Greek philosophers, both Aristotelians and Epicureans, are engaged, Bacon held, in fruitless controversies, for natural philosophy must produce works as well as hypotheses.[3] The scholastics are sunk in the depravity of Aristotle's dictatorship.[4] The atomists, though more bold, have merely exchanged one master for another.

Some, indeed, there have been who have gone more boldly to work, and taking it all for an open matter and giving their genius full play, have made a passage for themselves and their opinions by pulling down and demolishing former ones; and yet all their stir has but little advanced the matter, since their aim has been not to extend philosophy and the arts in substance and value, but only to change doctrines and transfer the kingdom of opinions to themselves.[5]

Others, probably Gilbert, have committed themselves to experience, but have, according to Bacon, become engrossed in a single discovery and proceeded aimlessly and without design.[6]

The *New Organon* was to be Bacon's antidote for the ills of philosophy. This new method of philosophizing was to establish certainty, in successive stages, through the evidence of the senses, guided as if through a machine.[7]

[1] Bacon, *Works*, XII, 387.
[2] Ibid., VIII, 18.
[3] Ibid., VIII, 26.
[4] Ibid., VIII, 39-30.
[5] Ibid., VIII, 30.
[6] Ibid., VIII, 31.
[7] Ibid., VIII, 61.

Now my method . . . is easy to explain; and it is this. I propose to establish progressive stages of certainty. The evidence of the sense, helped and guarded by a certain process of correction, I retain. But the mental operation which follows the act of sense I for the most part reject; and instead of it I open and lay out a new and certain path for the mind to proceed in, starting directly from the simple sensuous perception.[1]

There are only two ways, Bacon maintained in aphorism XIX of the *New Organon*, to discover truth. The first goes from the senses directly to general axioms from which are derived the middle axioms. The second, 'the true way', rises from sensuous perception of particulars, ascending continuously to the most general axioms. This latter way is the new organon.[2]

The new method was to have as its basis a redefinition of the old categories of form and matter. Indeed, all explanation was to be expressed in terms of the actions of material bodies, understood by recognition of their 'forms' or inner laws of activity.

For though in nature nothing really exists beside individual bodies, performing pure individual acts according to a fixed law, yet in philosophy this very law and the investigation, discovery and explanation of it, is the foundation as well of knowledge as of operation. And it is this law, with its causes, that I mean when I speak of *Forms*; a name which I the rather adopt because it has grown into use and become familiar.[3]

It is through *forms* that the natural philosopher understands the general causes of phenomena, and comprehends the unity of nature through its diversity.[4] This unity is not served by leaping into the hypotheses of the atomists, 'for that school is so busied with the particles that it hardly attends to the structure.'[5]

The atomic philosophy, of which Bacon was so lately a partisan, is still, he held, preferable to the Aristotelian, but it does not suffice.[6]

[M]en cease not from abstracting nature till they come to potential and unformed matter nor on the other hand from dissecting nature till they reach the atom; things which even if true, can do but little for the welfare of mankind.[7]

Nature, it is true, is to be dissected, both in the laboratory and in the mind, but the process must be kept close to parctice and certitude.[8]

For example, we must inquire what amount of spirit there is in every body, what of tangible essence; and of the spirit, whether it be copious or turgid, or meagre and scarce; whether it be fine or coarse, akin to air or to fire; brisk or sluggish,

---

[1] Bacon, *Works,* VIII, 60.   [2] Ibid., VIII, 71.   [3] Ibid., VIII, 168.
[4] Ibid., VIII, 167.   [5] Ibid., VIII, 85–6.   [6] Ibid., VIII, 103.
[7] Ibid., VIII, 97.   [8] Ibid., VIII, 175.

weak or strong, progressive or retrograde, interrupted or continuous, agreeing with external and surrounding objects or disagreeing &c. In like manner we must inquire into the tangible essence (which admits of no fewer differences than the spirit) into its coats, its fibres, its kinds of textures.[1]

Bacon's language has passed from that of the Greeks to that of the chemists. The new method leads, not to atoms, but to the spirits and grosser bodies which can actually be investigated through manipulation. Both pillars of the atomic philosophy—the immutable atom and the void—must be rejected.

Nor shall we thus be led to the doctrine of atoms, which implies the hypothesis of a vacuum and that of the unchangeableness of matter (both false assumptions); we shall be led only to real particles, such as really exist.[2]

Thus, matter is no longer to be thought of in terms of atoms and void, but rather in terms of *gross matter* and a material *activating spirit* which pervades all space.[3]

No known body in the upper parts of the earth is without a spirit. . . . For the cavities of tangible things do not admit of a vacuum, but are filled with air or the proper spirit of the thing. . . . [T]his spirit whereof I am speaking is . . . a body thin and invisible, and yet having place and dimension and are real . . . a rarefied body, akin to air, though greatly differing from it.[4]

The nature of Bacon's material spirits and the processes which they undergo provide the key to Bacon's later theory of matter. The spirit enveloped within tangible bodies is the cause of all natural operations.[5] The spirits of 'inanimate' bodies are mixed with the tangible parts like air in snow.[6] The material spirits differ from tangible matter in that they are absolutely light, having no weight but rather decrease the weight of the gross matter which they inhabit.[7] Spiritous matter, according to Bacon, is endowed with perception and appetition.[8]

Man's knowledge of nature, Bacon wrote in the *Sylva Sylvarum* (1627), has been limited by the grossness of his senses. This limitation has resulted in a paucity of knowledge concerning the material spirits.

The spirits or pneumaticals, that are in all tangible bodies are scarce known. Sometimes they take them for *vacuum*; whereas they are the most active of bodies. Sometimes they take them for air; from which they differ exceedingly. . . . And

---

[1] Bacon, *Works*, VIII, 176.   [2] Ibid., VIII, 177.
[3] Ibid., X, 262–3.   [4] Ibid., X, 156–7.
[5] Ibid., VIII, 275; X, 21, 83.   [6] Ibid., X, 159.
[7] Ibid., VIII, 278.   [8] Ibid., V, 63.

sometimes they will have them to be virtues or qualities of the tangible parts which they see; whereas they are things by themselves.[1]

Spirits are never at rest; from their processes spring all the effects of nature.[2] There are two types of spirits; the 'animate' and the lifeless. The vital spirit is always continuous whereas the inanimate spirits are 'cut off and surrounded by the grosser body which intercepts them'.[3] Inanimate spirits are nearly the same substance as air. Vital spirits are close to that of fire.[4]

The spirits interact with gross matter through various 'chemical' (non-mechanical) processes.

[I]n every tangible inanimate body the enclosed spirit first multiplies itself, and as it were feeds upon those tangible parts which are best disposed and prepared for that purpose; and so digests and elaborates and turns them into spirit; and then they escape altogether.[5]

These processes include concoction, colliquation, maturation, and rarefaction.[6] Spirits have two 'desires': one of self-multiplication, and another of attraction for like spirits.[7] The forms and qualities of tangible bodies result from the nature of these active spirits.

The native spirits also admit great diversity, as hot cold, active, dull &c. whence proceed most of the virtues and qualities (as we call them) of bodies.[8]

The mere presence or absence of the spirit of a body can account for its physical state.

[T]he spirit in a tangible substance, if discharged, contracts bodies and dries them up; if detained, softens and melts them; if neither wholly discharged nor wholly detained gives them shape, produces limbs, assimilates, digests, ejects, organizes and the like.[9]

When spirits are detained and expanded by heat, bodies are softened (e.g. white-hot iron), or become fluid (metals), or liquid (gum, wax).[10] Hardness is caused by the 'jejuneness of the spirits and their imparity with the tangible parts'.[11] Softer bodies contain a greater quantity of spirits which cause a more equal spreading of the tangible parts.[12] Fibrous bodies have a 'desire of continuance' and a 'greediness of moisture'.[13]

'The spirit in a body of firm texture', Bacon wrote, 'is detained, though against its will'.[14] Liquefaction is caused by the forced retention of spirits which 'play within the body and open it'.[15] Bodies which are difficult to

---

[1] Bacon, *Works*, IV, 219.   [2] Ibid., IV, 219; X, 21.   [3] Ibid., IV, 429–31; X, 159.
[4] Ibid., X, 161.   [5] Ibid., VIII, 275.   [6] Ibid., IV, 221; V, 80.
[7] Ibid., X, 262.   [8] Ibid., V, 83.   [9] Ibid., VIII, 275.
[10] Ibid., VIII, 276.   [11] Ibid., V, 85.   [12] Ibid., V, 85.
[13] Ibid., V, 85.   [14] Ibid., X, 166.   [15] Ibid., V, 82.

liquefy, are so because the spirits are easily emitted, whereby the tangible parts contract.[1] Fragile bodies contain a small quantity of spirits and is concomitant with porosity.[2]

It is seen, therefore, that Bacon's later theory of matter is one of the interaction of gross, visible parts of matter and invisible material spirits, both of which are physically mixed, as Bacon had it, like air in snow. Bacon's spirits are closer to Telesio's material spirits than to Descartes' subtle matter.[3] Indeed, Bacon's theory of matter offers some interesting contrasts to that of Descartes.

In Descartes' corpuscular philosophy, there are three elements. The first is of extremely fine, irregular particles which fill the spaces between coarser particles. The second is the '*matière subtile*' which is composed of coarser, spherical particles in motion. Finally, there are the still larger and more irregular particles of gross matter. All phenomena in nature are caused by the action of the motion of these various forms of matter.[4] The three Cartesian elements differ only in size and shape, whereas in Bacon there is an essential qualitative difference between spirit and tangible matter. The only properties of matter permitted in Descartes' theory are extension and motion; in that of Bacon, matter possesses appetition and perception. For Descartes, the only interaction between elements is that of collision; for Bacon, spirit and matter interact through concoction, colliquation and other non-mechanical processes. Fluidity in Descartes' mechanical philosophy is caused by the relative motion of the component particles; firmness by relative rest. Bacon accounted for fluidity and firmness by the mere presence or absence of the material spirit within the gross body. In sum, despite some interesting resemblances, Bacon's theory of matter and Descartes' corpuscular philosophy are essentially disparate.

It is often claimed by those who like to pick out 'modern' anticipations in past authors, that Bacon's conception of heat was truly modern and mechanical. Indeed, Bacon does appear to expound a type of kinetic theory of heat. The following passage, without the italicized part, is usually quoted.

When I say of Motion that it is as the genus of which heat is a species, I would be understood to mean, not that heat generates motion or that motion generates heat . . . but that Heat itself, its essence and quiddity, is Motion and nothing else; *limited however by the specific differences which I will presently subjoin.*[5]

[1] Bacon, *Works,* V, 82.
[2] Ibid., V, 83.
[3] Telesio, *De Rerum Natura* (Naples, 1570), *passim.* See Neil van Deusen, *Telesio* (New York, 1930), *passim.*
[4] René Descartes, *Oeuvres,* ed. V. Cousin (Paris, 1824), III, *passim.*
[5] Bacon, *Works,* VIII, 211. Emphasis supplied.

These limitations, almost always ignored, are important for the full understanding of Bacon's theory of heat. It is essential to stress that for Bacon, if *heat* is a mode of motion, so is *cold*. Heat is an expansive motion, and in an upward direction. Cold is also a motion, but contractive and downward.[1] As more motion implies more heat, increased motion in the opposite direction implies more cold. Thus, if one body has a quicker 'cold spirit' than another, it will, of course, be colder. Water, for example, is colder than oil because it has a 'quicker spirit' and snow is colder than water because it has more of it.[2] It is evident, therefore, that heat is not the measure of motion in Bacon's theory as in a kinetic theory, but that motion, depending upon its nature, is both heat and cold. Hence, Bacon's theory of heat and cold, while partially mechanical, is not so modern as some of his commentators imply.

Bacon's place in the history of atomism is complicated by his two opposing positions toward the atomic philosophy. During his lifetime and for many years afterwards, the earlier works favouring the atomic theory were not published. The *Novum Organum* (1620), the *Historia Vitae et Mortis* (1623), and the posthumous *Sylva Sylvarum* (1627) were the first major works to expound in great detail a theory of matter. These works of Bacon's mature period were all unfavourable to atomism. The major atomistic works of 1603–12, the *Cogitationes* and the *De Principiis*, were not published until 1653. Only the small essay 'Of Atheism' of 1612 hinted at his interest in atomism. The very fact, however, that the atomistic works did not appear until the 1650s played an interesting role in the acceptance of atomism in England.

Bacon left his manuscripts to William Boswell who was ambassador to the Netherlands from 1633 until his death circa 1649.[3] Boswell was closely linked to the Hobbes-Cavendish-Pell group; Pell was his 'affectionate friend' with whom he corresponded.[4] Boswell was greatly interested in the mechanical philosophy, and was familiar with the new developments in Paris.[5] It was in connexion with the new advances in the mechanical philosophy that Boswell had published, first Gilbert's *Philosophia Nova* in 1651 and Bacon's atomistic works and some others under the title *Scripta in Naturalia et Universalia Philosophia* in 1653.[6]

---

[1] Bacon *Works*, VIII, 212–14.
[2] Ibid., IV. 205.
[3] See Bacon's will in Bacon, *Life*, VII, 539.
[4] Boswell to Pell, 5 Aug. 1645, in Robert Vaughan, *Protectorate of Cromwell* (London, 1838), II, 369.
[5] Cavendish to Pell, 26 March, 1645, in Vaughan, II, 361.
[6] Boswell's friend Isaac Gruter actually published these works from Boswell's papers after the latter's death.

Boswell saw the close similarity between some of Gilbert's speculations in the manuscripts of the *Philosophia Nova* and some of the later speculations of the Paris and Leiden mechanical philosophers. He was very interested in adding new material to the discussions, and in safeguarding the priority of his late countryman, Gilbert. He wrote to Pell in 1648:

I pray, do you think Gilbert's Physiologia MS (which I believe you have seen in the King's Library at St. James's) would make anything to his or the renown of our nation, if printed in these wild times. I find that he had the start of many of our modern madcaps, and so may challenge precedence![1]

Apparently Boswell decided to proceed; after his death his friend Gruter published an edition of the *Philosophia Nova* in quarto in 1651.[2] It was probably the same reasons which motivated him to consider placing before the scientific world a 'new' Bacon. The 1640s and 1650s marked a revival of interest in atomism in England and on the continent. Many of the new theories, like that of Gassend and others, were re-workings of the atomism of antiquity. Boswell probably saw in Bacon's atomic treatises, which were in his possession in manuscript form, much of what was then thought to be original. In order to further Bacon's good name, and more probably, in order to establish *English* precedence in the revival of atomism, Boswell (through Gruter) worked to publish Bacon's atomic works in 1653. Hence Bacon, despite his mature opposition to atomism, through the publication of his atomic works at a crucial time contributed to the acceptance of atomism in England.

[1] Boswell to Pell, Jan. 1648, in Vaughan, II, 376–7.
[2] William Gilbert, *De Mundo Nostro Sublunari Philosophia Nova* (Amsterdam, 1651).

VI
THOMAS HOBBES AND
THE MECHANICAL PHILOSOPHY

ONE of the first (and most talented) Englishmen to treat all phases of the mechanical philosophy systematically was Thomas Hobbes. A figure of intellectual dash and verve, Hobbes has been subjected to the minutest of scrutiny. Yet, historians of science have invariably relegated him to a secondary position. Perhaps Hobbes' disagreements with Boyle and others, and his failure to gain recognition by the Royal Society have obscured his true significance as a natural philosopher. Hobbes was one of the three most important mechanical philosophers of the mid-seventeenth century, along with Descartes and Gassend. His atomism, moreover, played a significant role, both within his own system, and in controversies both scientific and theological.

The atomism of Thomas Hobbes, like that of Bacon, is treated with much ambiguity in the literature of the history of science. The source of the confusion is obvious: Hobbes' thought on the constitution of matter changed markedly in the course of his long career. By the time of the publication of the *De Corpore* in 1655, Hobbes had adopted a position quite unlike classical and contemporary atomists. Yet Hobbes played a major role in the establishment in England of atomism and the mechanical philosophy.

The mechanical philosophy of Hobbes is the subject of a long and excellent investigation by Frithiof Brandt.[1] Brandt's treatise, originally published in Danish and rendered almost unreadable by an unfortunate translation, is an extended search into the origins, development, and meaning of Hobbes' mechanism. It is not our purpose here to rival or replace the substance of that book. The pages following will stress Hobbes' historical relationship with English atomism, a topic left virtually untouched by Brandt, by Lasswitz' *Geschichte der Atomistik*, and by almost all other commentators.[2]

From 1630, when he began instructing the Earl of Newcastle (later

[1] Frithiof Brandt, *Thomas Hobbes' Mechanical Conception of Nature,* trans. V. Maxwell and A. Fausbell (Copenhagen and London, 1928).
[2] Charles Harrison's 'Bacon, Hobbes, Boyle and the Ancient Atomists', *Harvard Studies and Notes in Philology and Literature* 15 (1933) 191–213, broaches the subject, but is sketchy and takes no cognizance of Hobbes' evolution.

Marquis and Duke) and his brother Sir Charles Cavendish in the mysteries of natural philosophy, to 1655 when his major physical work, *De Corpore*, appeared, Hobbes' theory of matter underwent a number of alterations. Several documents stand out as essential to the understanding of this evolution: the 'little treatise' (about 1630), Charles Cavendish's report to Jungius (1645), a letter to Mersenne (1648), and the *De Corpore* (1655). The 'little treatise' was published for the first time in 1889 by Ferdinand Tönnies as an appendix to Hobbes' *Elements of Law*.[1]

The first section of the 'little treatise' contains the fundamental principles of its philosophy, defining *agent, patient, species, substance,* and *accident.* With these definitions, and the concept of motion, Hobbes proposed to build the framework of his thought.

In the tract, Hobbes wished to investigate the action of one substance (agent) upon another (patient). This action can occur, he wrote, in two possible ways: through the working of the medium, or through an effluvium, presumably corporeal, although this was not made explicit.[2] He rejected out of hand a complete reliance on a medium, and insisted that some agents, though not all, are effective through the emission of species or effluvia.[3] The laws of species emission are simple: 'Species the farther they gow from the body whence they issue, the weaker they are,' although they 'procede infinitely'.[4] They travel in straight lines; when different species arrive at one observer *in the same line,* they are perceived as one. For example, when white light passes through red glass, the emerging light appears red, although it is in reality the mixture of white and red effluvia. Hence, Hobbes concluded, colour is light which includes the species of diverse bodies.[5] Certain species, depending upon their nature, both attract and repel each other; this is the manner in which the lodestone attracts iron. The species of the lodestone commingles with the species of iron. The latter is made swifter and more abundant, and hence is drawn towards the lodestone.[6]

With the 'little treatise' Hobbes took his first important steps away from scholasticism. Stripped from his analysis were the Aristotelian forms and qualities; all that remained were the medium and corporeal species acting between patient and agent. In the 'little treatise' one can discern the germ of a mechanical philosophy. By 1636, the nature of Hobbes' mechanism matured and became more sophisticated. The Earl of Newcastle and Hobbes were, in the 1630s, speculating upon matter and motion in a

[1] T. Hobbes, *Elements of Law*, ed. F. Tönnies (London, 1889), pp. 193–210. Henceforth cited as *Elements*. I have used a later (Cambridge, 1928) edition.
[2] Ibid., p. 156.
[3] Ibid., pp. 156–7.
[4] Ibid., p. 157.   [5] Ibid., p. 158.   [6] Ibid., p. 160.

manner that can only be termed 'mechanical'. Hobbes wrote to Newcastle on 29 July 1636:

> In thinges that are not demonstrable, of which kind is the part of naturall philosophy as depending upon the motion of bodies so subtile as they are invisible, such as are ayre and spirits, the most that can be attayned unto is to have such opinions as no certayne experience can confute, and from which can be deduced by lawfull argumentation no absurdity, and such are your Lordships opinions in your letter of the 3rd of July which I had the honor to receave last weeke, namely. That the variety of thinges is but variety of locall motion in the spirits or invisible partes of bodies. And that such motion is heate.[1]

The sources of these opinions of Hobbes and Newcastle are obscure. Undoubtedly, as Brandt maintains, most of Hobbes' thought was *sui generis*. The notion of 'ayres and spirits' was probably, however, drawn from Bacon, as was also the idea that local motion is heat. It is possible also, although no direct evidence exists, that Hariot's atomism was known to Hobbes and Newcastle through Newcastle's brother Charles Cavendish, Walter Warner, and John Pell.[2]

In 1645, Sir Charles Cavendish wrote a letter to Joachim Jungius, the German natural philosopher, describing the latest developments in Hobbes' evolution. It can be seen that by 1645 Hobbes had refined and enriched his earlier thought. For the first time, one can detect the emergence of a *system*.

Most of Cavendish's report is concerned with Hobbes' definition of place, space, and movement. 'Space is simply a phantasm of a body. He [Hobbes] adds "simply" because it has nothing to do with the nature of space whether the imagined body is white to black or warm or cold.'[3] Cavendish then proceeded to describe the basic mechanical principles of the Hobbesian system. In the first place, a movement in any body can be induced only by an external mover. '[N]othing moves by itself.'[4] Secondly, the movement induced can only be stopped or diminished by the opposing motion of an external mover. Each body which acts as a mover is also moved. All change in nature results from movements of the invisible parts of bodies. 'The cause of all motion and all change is motion.'[5] Even the cause of *rest* is motion. Rest itself cannot be the cause of motion, of change of motion, or of rest. It is probable that Hobbes, through Cavendish, was here scoffing at his adversary Descartes, who explained solidity, for example, by the mutual rest of the component particles.

---

[1] Hobbes to Newcastle, 29 July, 1636, in Historical Manuscripts Commission, *Portland Manuscripts* (London, 1891), II, p. 128.

[2] See above, Chapter IV.

[3] Cay von Brockdorff, *Des Sir Charles Cavendishs Bericht für Joachim Jungius* (Kiel, 1934), p. 3.

[4] Ibid., p. 3.   [5] Ibid., p. 3.

Cavendish went on to explain Hobbes' theory of hardness, probably the first truly kinetic notion of hardness in the seventeenth century. A body is hard because of the rapid motions of the invisible parts of that body. These motions can be vibratory, circular, or elliptical. The hardness increases as the swiftness of the motion of the component particles increases.[1]

The document (Cavendish's report) is tantalizing, and does not completely satisfy the eager student. What, for example, are these 'invisible bodies'? Are they true atoms or are they infinitely divisible? What were Hobbes' views on the existence of a vacuum? Fortunately, some of these questions can be resolved by recourse to letters and fragments dating from the same period.

In 1646, Hobbes explained certain of his views in an optical draught dedicated to William Cavendish, recently elevated to Marquis of Newcastle. A vacuum, one of the pillars of the atomic philosophy, is explicitly admitted by Hobbes for what may be the first time.

I suppose [Hobbes wrote] that there is vacuity made by such dilation [of the sun] but find no impossibility in admitting vacuity, for no probable argument hath ever been produced to the contrary.[2]

In an obvious reference to Descartes, he denigrated the idea that extension and body are identical. '[W]ho knows not that Extension is one thing and the thing extended another, as hunger is one thing, and that which is hungry another.'[3]

A later letter to Mersenne confirmed Hobbes' vacuist position. 'Also, about the vacuum', Hobbes wrote, 'my opinion is the same as before: there exist very small spaces [*minima loca*] now here, now there, in which there is no body . . . [for the action of bodies] is such that they put into motion neighbouring bodies, and by these collisions scatter the particles about; an action which necessarily results in certain void spaces.'[4]

In this period, Hobbes' theory of matter was the following: the universe admits of void space and matter. All gross bodies are composed of small invisible subtle bodies whose varieties of motion accounted for the various physical qualities to be found in nature. If in Descartes the stress was upon *extension*, in Hobbes it was placed upon *motion*. To be sure, both matter and movement accounted for phenomena, but in the work of Hobbes, the emphasis was decidedly upon the latter; Brandt calls Hobbes by the very

[1] Brockdorff, p. 3.
[2] M. Köhler, 'Studien zur Naturphilosophie des Thomas Hobbes', *Arch. Gesch. Phil.* 16 (1902–03) 72.
[3] Ibid., p. 72.
[4] Hobbes to Mersenne, 17 February, 1648, in F. Tönnies, 'Hobbes Analekten II', *Arch. Gesch. Phil.* 19 (1905–06) 172; Tönnies. 'Contributions à l'historie de la pensée de Hobbes', *Arch. Phil.* 12 (1936) 260–1.

appropriate term 'motionalist'. This stress upon motion was continued in Hobbes' major physical treatise, *De Corpore*, which appeared, after much delay, in 1655.

The untold story of the circumstances surrounding the publication of the *De Corpore* would be a fascinating and enlightening one. Unfortunately, at the present time, there do not exist sufficient materials with which to tell it. It is known, however, that Hobbes was working on drafts of it all during the 1640s; earlier accounts of Hobbes' philosophy, as for example Cavendish's report, show marked resemblances to the 1655 work.[1] His friends, Charles Cavendish and Pell, urged him throughout the 1640's to publish it. 'Mr. Hobbes', Cavendish wrote in 1644, 'puts me in hope of his philosophie which he writes is now putting in order, but I feare that will take a longe time'.[2] By the end of 1646, Hobbes was still at work. Cavendish wrote to Pell that 'Mr. Hobbes reads mathematics sometimes to our prince, but I beleeve he hath spare time enough besides to go on with his philosophy.'[3]

Had Hobbes not delayed, his *De Corpore* would doubtlessly have advocated the vacuist position. Instead, by 1655, Hobbes had assumed a plenist viewpoint. What had shaken him from the views which he held in 1648? The question remains a tantalizing mystery, but it is possible that Hobbes saw in the all-pervading fluid aether which he introduced in 1655 a single mechanical instrument which was very much simpler to apply than a complex of effluvial mechanisms.

The theme of the *De Corpore* is the workings of matter and motion, and especially the latter, knowledge of which is the 'gate of natural philosophy universal'.[4] The one comprehensive cause of all effects in nature is motion.[5]

For the variety of all figures arises out of the variety of these motions by which they are made; and motion cannot be understood to have any other cause besides motion; nor has the variety of those things we perceive by sense, as of *colours*, *sounds*, savours, etc. any other cause than motion, residing partly in the objects that work upon our and partly in ourselves.[6]

The above passage is a concise and accurate statement of the basis of Hobbesian natural philosophy.

In the section entitled 'Physics', Hobbes outlined his world-view. The universe, Hobbes held, is composed of visible bodies, such as the earth

[1] See also R. I. Aaron, 'Possible Draft of *De Corpore*', *Mind* 54 (1945) 342–56 and Jean Jacquot, 'Notes on an Unpublished Work of Thomas Hobbes', *Notes Rec. R. Soc. Lond.* 9 (1952) 188–95 and 'Un document inédit', *Thale's* 8 (1952) 33–86.
[2] C. Cavendish to Pell. 17 Dec. 1644, in Halliwell, *Collection*, p. 87.
[3] Cavendish to Pell, 12 Oct. 1646, in Vaughan, II, p. 371.
[4] Thomas Hobbes, *English Works*, ed. Sir William Molesworth (London, 1839–45), I, viii. Henceforth cited as *Works*.
[5] Ibid. I, 69.   [6] Ibid., I, 69–70.

and moon, invisible bodies such 'as the small atoms which are disseminated through the whole space between the earth and the stars', and the fluid aether 'which so fills all the rest of the universe, as that it leaves in it no empty place at all'.[1] The atoms are small, imperceptible bodies in motion. Hobbes' atoms differ from those of Gassend, for example, in that there exist gradations in hardness among them: some atoms are hard, others less so, and still others quite soft.[2] These atoms are indefinitely divisible, by God and by reason,[3] but are not so in nature.

The atoms, according to Hobbes, congregate to form bodies which differ from each other in consistency, magnitude, motion, and figure.[4] When the motion of the ambient ether expands the internal parts of a body, that body becomes hot. When the ether forces an inward, contractive motion, the body becomes cold.[5]

Hardness, in the new Hobbesian system, is a quality which owes its existence to several causes. If the harder atoms cleave together, the resultant body will be hard. Thus, if a soft body be made of both hard atoms and softer 'fluid' particles, it may be made hard by the exhalation of the softer parts. Secondly, if hard atoms in rapid motion are enclosed in a small space, the resultant 'body' will appear hard. This latter notion of hardness was the one which Hobbes held in the 1640s.[6] A fluid may be fluid of itself, and may be as homogeneous as a fluid on the atomic level, and need not, as the true atomists had maintained, be made of hard particles.[7] 'I understand by *fluidity*', Hobbes wrote in the *De Corpore*, 'that which is made such by nature equally in every part of the fluid body'.[8]

The ambient aethereal medium is the mechanical agency for the production of physical phenomena. Sounds are created by the motion of the medium upon the ear. Odours 'must necessarily proceed from some mutation in the organ, and all mutation is motion'.[9] The cause of odour is the motion of the invisible parts of the odouriferous body, without any efflux, the motion being propagated to the nose by the medium. Gravity is the motion towards the centre of the earth by 'heavy' bodies. The earth itself 'attracteth heavy bodies' to its centre.[10] in a very complicated manner utilizing the air and diurnal motion of the earth.[11] Hobbes predicted on the basis of his theory that there would be no descent at the poles 'which whether it be true or false, experience must determine'.[12]

Hobbes repudiated his earlier (1630) reliance upon effluvia; by 1655 he relied totally upon the medium. His rejection of the vacuum was probably connected with this. The existence of a vacuum would nullify many of

[1] Hobbes, *Works,* 426. [2] Ibid., I, 427. [3] Ibid., I, 445–6.
[4] Ibid., I, 445. [5] Ibid., I, 466–7. [6] Ibid., I, 476–7.
[7] Ibid., I, 417. [8] Ibid., I, 426. [9] Ibid., I, 302.
[10] Ibid., I, 510. [11] Ibid., I, 512–13. [12] Ibid., I, 513.

Hobbes' mechanisms, including gravity, heat, and cold. The simplicity and elegance of the aether mechanisms probably caused Hobbes to abandon the vacuum and effluvia, the latter being components of a theory which is admittedly more cumbersome and complex.

Because of the rejection of his former vacuist position, Hobbes' views in the 1640s have been unjustifiably neglected by historians. The decade following 1640 marked a high point of Hobbes' philosophical vigour. It was during these years that Hobbes' influence over the growing New-castle Circle and its associates was most potent.

During the 1640s, Hobbes became a close friend of Pierre Gassend, the French reviver of Epicurus. Gassend's first major presentation of his atomistphysics was in his *Animadversiones in decimum librum Diogenis Laertii* of 1649.[1] Hobbes had already seen manuscript version of it in 1644, and reported to Charles Cavendish that 'it is as big as Aristotle's philosophie, but much truer and excellent Latin.'[2] In the same year he saw manuscripts of Descartes' *Principia Philosophiae* which did not please him.[3] Cavendish reported to Pell 'that Gassendes and De Cartes are of different dispositions and I perceive Mr. Hobbes joines with Gassendes in his dislike of De Cartes his writings, for he utterlie mislikes De Cartes his last newe booke of philo-sophie which by his leave I highlie esteeme of.'[4] He further wrote that Hobbes 'is joined in a greate friendship with Gassendes'.[5] This friendship for Gassend, and admiration for his work on the part of Hobbes was not unimportant. Hobbes carried great weight with all the members of the Newcastle Circle, and it was probably through his influence that the irrepressible Margaret Cavendish (Marchioness and later Duchess of New-castle), William Petty, and Hobbes' friend Walter Charleton first became interested in the Epicurean atomism of Gassend.[6] Partly through these figures, and some others of the Newcastle Circle, atomism made its re-entry into England.

However, before atomism could be established as an acceptable natural philosophy in England, it had to overcome two very strong types of opposition: from the Aristotelians, and from theologians who were con-cerned with the atheistic implications of the atomic philosophy.[7] Hobbes' own vehement materialism only added to the burdens of the atomists.

Our interest in Hobbes' involvement with theological questions largely centres around his notion of *spirit* and its materiality—a subject of grave debate in mid-seventeenth-century England. Hobbes did not admit the presence of immaterial (and therefore immortal) substances in his universe.

[1] Pierre Gassend, *Animadversiones in decimum librum Diogenis Laertii* (Lyons, 1649).
[2] C. Cavendish to Pell, 10 October 1644, in Halliwell, *Collection*, p. 85.
[3] Ibid., p. 85.　　　　　　[4] Ibid., p. 86.　　　　　　[5] Ibid., p. 87.
[6] See below, Chapters VII and VIII.　　　　　　[7] See below, Chapter VIII.

In an attempt to exorcise all occult qualities from natural philosophy, Hobbes wished to be rid of the vague notion of incorporeal spirit as cause. Instead, he defined *spirit* is a manner very similar to that of Bacon. In *Of Human Nature* (written 1640, published 1650), Hobbes wrote:

By the name of *spirit,* we understand a *body natural,* but of such subtility that it worketh not upon the senses; but that filleth up the place which the image of a visible body might fill up.[1]

That there exist *immaterial* spirits is a flat contradiction in terms, for a spirit is a substance, and all substances have dimension and corporeality.

Those who refer to scripture to support the immateriality of the soul Hobbes held to be in error. The scriptures, he maintained, say nothing of the soul's incorporeality.

But though the Scripture acknowledges spirits [Hobbes wrote] yet doth it nowhere say that they are incorporeal, meaning thereby without dimension and quality; nor I think, is that word incorporeal at all in the Bible.[2]

Or the human spirit, Hobbes reported, the Bible says only that it comes, goes, and dwells in man, 'all of which words do imply *locality*; and locality is *dimension*; and whatsoever hath dimension is *body* be it never so subtile'.[3] Hobbes, therefore, like the ancient atomists, supported the materiality of the soul, and to compound his crime quoted scripture to support it:

To me therefore it seemeth that the Scripture favoureth them more than hold angels and spirits corporeal, than those than hold the contrary.[4]

In his widely read *Leviathan* (1951), Hobbes continued along these lines. He denied that scripture supports the natural immortality of the soul,[5] or that it says that man has anything but a corporeal spirit.[6]

Substance and *body* [he wrote] signify the same thing; and therefore *substance incorporeal* are words, which when they are joined together destroy one another, as if a man should say incorporeal body.[7]

Since Hobbes admitted that God is a substance,[8] and that all substances are bodies, a simple syllogism would bring Hobbes to the position that even *God* is corporeal, a logical step, however, which he did not explicitly take for many years.[9] Still, he was willing to state quite openly that angels and spirits, if anything at all, are material, and to deny that man's body is inhabited by them.[10]

[1] Hobbes, *Works,* IV, 60–61.
[2] Ibid., IV, 61.   [3] Ibid., IV, 62.   [4] Ibid., IV, 62.
[5] Thomas Hobbes, *Leviathan,* ed. Michael Oakeshott (Oxford, 1960), p. 410.
[6] Ibid., pp. 421–2.   [7] Ibid., p. 256.
[8] René Descartes, *Philosophical Works,* ed. E. S. Haldane and G. R. T. Ross (New York, 1955), II, 72.
[9] A discussion of this problem can be found in David Kubrin, 'Spirit and Matter in Hobbes' Mechanical Philosophy', to appear.
[10] Hobbes, *Leviathan,* pp. 420–1.

Hobbes' position on the materiality of spirits created a furore in England, and embarrassed such pious friends as Walter Charleton. Aubrey reported that the bishops in Parliament wished to have Hobbes burnt as a heretic.[1] Hobbes was attacked as an Epicurean, atomist, Anthropomorphist, Sadducean, Manichean, Luciferian, and Jew.[2] The renowned Henry More attacked '*Hobbes* that confident Exploder of Immaterial Substances out of the world'.[3]

Hobbes' notoriety deeply affected the fortunes of atomism in England. He made the paganism of the ancient atomic philosophy a living, burning issue in mid-seventeenth-century England. The task of purifying atomism from its ancient stigma of atheism was difficult enough, Hobbes added the bulk of his unorthodoxy to it. His friends were forced to dissociate themselves from his position in order to gain a respectable place for atomism in natural philosophy.[4] The battle for atomism was begun in the shadow of Hobbes.

[1] Aubrey, *Lives,* I, 339.
[2] Samuel Mintz, *Hunting of Leviathan* (Cambridge, 1962), pp. 40–41.
[3] Henry More, *Immortality of the Soul* (London, 1659), bk. 1, ch. X, p. 39.
[4] See below, Chapter VIII.

VII

DESCARTES, GASSEND, AND THE NEWCASTLE CIRCLE

UP TO this point, we have concentrated upon the purely English development of atomism from Hariot through Hobbes. The earlier atomic doctrines of Hariot and the Northumberland coterie failed, for various reasons outlined above, to take root in England and gain widespread acceptance. Through Thomas Hobbes and a group of English *emigrés*—the New castle Circle—atomism again became, in the 1640s, a living issue in English natural philosophy. The centre of this *emigré* activity was Paris; the leading figures of the group (Hobbes, Charles Cavendish, William Cavendish, then Marquis of Newcastle, and John Pell who was in the Netherlands) were in close contact with the French giants of the mechanical philosophy—Descartes and Gassend. Through correspondence, published works, and personal contact, the ideas of these two mingled with the already 'mechanical' inclinations of the Englishmen.

The infusion of Cartesian and Gassendist ideas into English atomism greatly changed it. Henceforth, English atomism borrowed heavily from both, often preferring to stress the similarities between the two, rather than their differences. The English atomists, even from the beginning of the century, were interested in explaining all phenomena by the action of matter in motion, rather than by reference to scholastic 'principles' or 'forms'.[1] They were, with some exceptions, delighted with the great new systems put forth by the two great French philosophers, and eagerly adapted the new concepts and mechanisms to fit their needs. The English natural philosophers were largely interested in the numerous mechanisms proposed as explanations of the physical qualities of bodies, mechanisms which they found in abundance in the works of both Descartes and Gassend. These new mechanisms added powerful plausibility and systematic coherence to the endeavour upon which they had already begun—the move to establish the primacy of explanation involving only matter in motion.

The system of Descartes is the subject of an enormous literature, including a large number of works which treat primarily of the physical aspects.

[1] See above, Chapters III and VI.

It will be of use, however, to review some of the salient points of his mechanical philosophy.

The universe, according to Descartes, is made of prime matter, whose only essential characteristic is its extension. There are no other necessary properties of substances but length, breadth, and depth.

The nature of matter or body . . . [Descartes wrote in his *Principia Philosophiae* of 1644] in general does not at all consist in hardness, or gravity or colour or that which is sensible in another manner, but alone in length, width and depth.[1]

Space, too, is extended, and therefore differs from body only in the imagination.[2] There can, consequently, be no space in the universe which is void.[3]

According to Descartes, the universal plenum is not divided, as some would have it, into atoms. Matter is indefinitely divisible, by God and by reason,[4] although in nature, the prime matter exists as hard corpuscles which can be considered difficult to divide. The prime matter is differentiated into several kinds by motion.[5] There are three types: a fine dust which gets between the interstices of larger corpuscles and permits no void, larger but still subtle round particles (*matière subtile* or aether) and, finally, relatively larger particles composing gross matter.[6] The three 'elements' differ only in size and motion, and are interconvertible.[7] All corpuscles are in motion, a movement bestowed upon them by God; the sum of this motion is constant.[8]

In the Cartesian system, all physical qualities depend upon the motion of these three kinds of matter,[9] each smaller particle playing a role in the motion of the larger. The hardness of a body is an effect of the mutual rest of its component corpuscles. 'I do not believe', wrote Descartes, 'that one can imagine a cement more suitable to join together the parts of hard bodies than their own repose'.[10] A fluid body, on the other hand, is composed of particles which are easily moved by the subtile matter because of their size and shape.[11] Heat is caused by the motion of the corpuscles of the third matter when excited by particles of the first.[12]

According to Descartes, the four elements of the scholastics are, in fact, composed of corpuscles whose magnitude, figure, and motion determine

---

[1] Descartes, *Oeuvres*, III, p. 123. Cousin's edition renders the *Principia* into modern French; see also the Latin edition of C. Adam and P. Tannery (Paris, 1897–1919), VIII, 1–348.

[2] Descartes, *Oeuvres*, III, 128.   [3] Ibid., III, 133.

[4] Ibid., III, 137, 149.   [5] Ibid., III, 138–9.

[6] Ibid., III, 217.   [7] Ibid., III, 334–5.

[8] Ibid., III, 150.   [9] Ibid., III, 139.

[10] Ibid., III, 167.   [11] Ibid., III, 168–9.

[12] Ibid., III, 352–3.

the properties of these elements. 'Air is nothing else but a mass of particles of the third element which are unbound and thus detached one from another so that they yield to all movements of the celestial matter which is among them; which is the reason that it is rare, liquid, and transparent.'[1] Air particles are almost all soft and flexible, like feathers of the tips of slender strings.[2] Water is composed of two sorts of particles both of which are long and slender. The first type is soft and pliant, and the second is rigid and inflexible; the former composes sweet water and the latter forms saline water.[3]

Earth, Descartes wrote, is composed of all sorts of gross corpuscles. Because of their size, the aether does not have the force to carry them with it (as it does air and water particles) but has enough to press them towards the earth, rendering them heavy.[4] All terrestrial matter may become fire particles when it is separated by the first type of matter and constrained to follow it, just as it becomes air when it follows the second type of matter. The principal difference between air and fire is that the particles of fire move more rapidly owing to the incomparably greater agitation of the first element compared with that of the second.[5]

Descartes' theory of matter rests entirely upon extension (or body) and its motion. 'All the diversity of forms which we meet', he wrote, 'depends upon local motion'.[6] This motion is transferred through collision, the laws of which Descartes presented as 'laws of nature'.[7] In a strict sense, therefore, Descartes' was a *mechanical* philosophy: it ultimately depended upon laws of mechanics. Another 'mechanical philosophy', in that it rested entirely upon matter and its motion, was that of Pierre Gassend, the French priest who was well known as an astronomer, mathematician, and natural philosopher.[8]

Gassend was the chief reviver of the system of Epicurus and Lucretius. From 1629, when he published his *Exercitationes paradoxicae adversus Aristotelos* to his death in 1655, Gassend worked upon a synthesis and adaptation of Epicurean philosophy, a labour which was crowned by his *Syntagma philosophicum*, first published in the posthumous *Opera Omnia* of 1658.[9] The appearance of the *Syntagma philosophicum* was preceded in 1649 by the important *Animadversiones in decimum librum Diogenis Laertii* to which

[1] Descartes, *Oeuvres,* III, 368–9. [2] Ibid., III, 369.
[3] Ibid., III, 370. [4] Ibid., III, 378.
[5] Ibid., III, 396. [6] Ibid., III, 139.
[7] Ibid., III, 152.
[8] There is an enormous literature on Gassend as a natural philosopher. Among the more reliable are Gaston Sortais, *Philosophie moderne depuis Bacon jusqu'à Leibniz,* 2 vols. (Paris, 1922); B. Rochot, *Les travaux de Gassendi* (Paris, 1944); and R. Lindsay, 'Pierre Gassendi and the Revival of Atomism in the Renaissance', *Am. J. Phys.* 13 (1945) 235–42.
[9] Pierre Gassend, *Opera Omnia* (Lyons, 1658).

was appended the relatively short *Philosophiae Epicuri syntagma*. There has been a great deal of confusion about these works. In *Robert Boyle and Seventeenth-Century Chemistry*, Marie Boas states that Gassend's 'final synthesis appeared only in 1658, too late to be as influential as it might have been otherwise'.[1] According to Miss Boas, before 1658 Boyle and others read only the small '*Philosophica Epicuri Syntagma [sic]*'.[2] In a recent article, Miss Boas (Mrs. A. R. Hall) insisted that Gassend's '*Philosophiae Epicuri Syntagma* of 1649 was only a small collection of atomic texts, and the real doctrine of Gassendi's interpretation had to wait for posthumous publication . . . until 1658, too late to be of importance to science.'[3] Similarly, A. R. Hall in *From Galileo to Newton* wrote: 'His [Gassend's] major work, *Syntagma Philosophiae* ('The System of Philosophy'), was published in 1658, too late to be effective. . . .'[4]

Neither Marie Boas Hall nor A. R. Hall mention the *Animadversiones* of 1649; this omission is unfortunate. This work was the first major presentation in systematic form of Gassend's physics. It is a mistake to claim, as the Halls have done, that Gassend's mechanical philosophy had to wait until 1658 for a full exposition. Both the *Animadversiones* of 1649 and the *Syntagma philosophicum* of 1658 have long sections subtitled '*pars physica*'. If one compares the two sections one can see that they are virtually the same. In fact, the parts dealing with the mechanical origins of the qualities of bodies are identical, word for word. The physics of the *Animadversiones* has twice as many pages as that of the *Syntagma philosophicum*, for the latter is printed in two columns and contains twice as much text per page.[5]

Since Gassend's physics was available during the 1650s, it was not 'too late' to have been influential. It was on the contrary very influential indeed as will be shown below.

During the 1640s, Gassend was in close contact with the Newcastle circle, the members of which eagerly received his published works.[6] It was, to a very large extent, through the members of this group, and especially

[1] Marie Boas, *Robert Boyle and Seventeenth Century Chemistry* (Cambridge, 1958), p. 80. Henceforth cited as *Boyle*.

[2] M. Boas, *Boyle*, p. 28.

[3] M. Boas Hall, 'Matter in 17th Century Science', in *Concept of Matter*, ed. Ernan McMullin (Notre Dame, 1963), p. 346.

[4] A. R. Hall, *From Galileo to Newton 1630–1720* (New York, 1963), p. 223. Hall is apparently referring to the *Syntagma philosophicum*, and not to a *Syntagma Philosophiae*, a title which belongs to no work of Gassend.

[5] Pierre Gassend, *Animadversiones in decimum librum Diogenis Laertii* (Lyons, 1649), I, 159–755, and *Opera*, I, 125–495. Henceforth cited as *Animadversiones*.

[6] See Jean Jacquot, 'Sir Charles Cavendish and his Learned Friends', *Ann. Sci.* **8** (1952) 13–28, 175–92; and Helen Hervey, 'Hobbes and Descartes in the Light of the Correspondence Between Sir Charles Cavendish and Dr. John Pell', *Osiris* **10** (1952) 67–91.

Hobbes (Gassend's good friend), that certain circles in England became aware of Gassend's physics.

The starting point for Gassend's physics is an ancient proposition: *Ex nihilo nihil fieri.* After the creation, in nature, Gassend claimed, this rule is valid, for once God created the prime matter, nothing else was or could be generated. With this reservation, Gassend turned to the atomism of Epicurus, based upon small, hard atoms and the void. The void, according to Gassend, exists in two forms: an extended vacuum outside the world, and a *vacuum coacervatum* or disseminated void, within.[1] All natural phenomena in Gassend's system are explained employing only atoms and their motions in the void.

The indivisible atoms themselves have the following essential properties: magnitude and figure, hardness (since each is a plenum), and gravity (*pondus*) or principle of motion.[2] The *impetus* or *energia* of all the atoms, by which Gassend means the active force in collision, is constant and is as it was at the creation. Unlike Epicurus, Gassend's atoms have motions in all directions. The *vis motrix* or principle of motion is essential to matter and was bestowed upon it at the creation by God.[3]

The atoms, through their motions and shapes, form *moleculae* or corpuscles of varying sizes, shapes, and motions. The qualities of gross bodies, such as fluidity, firmness, etc. depend upon these prior qualities of the atoms and their concretions. Whereas by 1655 Hobbes turned to explanations utilizing the medium as mechanism, Gassend relied upon the action of effluvia. Electrical and magnetic attraction, for instance, are caused by exhalations from the attracting bodies of appropriate streams of small corpuscles.[4]

Firmness or solidity, Gassend held, results from the grossness and complicated shapes of the corpuscles causing them to be interlaced and difficult to move. Fluidity results from the ease of motion of the corpuscles because of their regular shapes and relative lightness.[5] A body is heated by fire because of the ingress and motion of 'calorific atoms' which are small, light, round, and very swift.[6] *Cold* which itself is a 'true and positive quality' is caused by the ingress of 'frigorific atoms' or heavy, slow particles which are not easily moved.

The system of Gassend, the Catholic priest, and that of Epicurus, the pagan, have important differences. The French priest wished to exorcise from Epicurean atomism its atheistic implications. First, according to Gassend, the universe requires, *contra Epicurus*, the existence of God. God created the universe, and with it the atoms which were, therefore, not

---

[1] Gassend, *Animadversiones,* I, 169–77; 297–303.   [2] Ibid., I, 201.
[3] Ibid., I, 273.   [4] Ibid., I, 347–62.
[5] Ibid., I, 331–8.   [6] Ibid., I, 319.

eternally existent. Moreover, God continually regulates the universe; He is not an absentee Lord.[1] He bestows upon man, Gassend held in opposition to both Epicurus and Hobbes, an immaterial and immortal soul. With these revisions, Epicurean atomism can thus be purged of its atheism.

The differences between the systems of Descartes and Gassend are obvious; the similarities, on the other hand, are greater than one would at first suspect. Both systems explain all phenomena in nature by matter and its motion. Each system is essentially an 'impact' physics, despite Gassend's use of subtle threads and other devices. Descartes' 'laws of nature' for example are collision rules. The plenum-vacuum disparity, therefore, tends to be obscured. Descartes' plenum appears very much like the interspersed void of Gassend with respect to the motion and collision of matter,[2] i.e. a space containing celestial matter has properties similar to the Gassendist vacuum. Moreover, there was basically some ground for agreement even on the question of the divisibility of matter. Descartes maintained the indefinite divisibility of matter by God and by mathematical analysis; Gassend agreed with this position. But, Gassend held, in nature atoms were indivisible. Although Descartes' corpuscles were not indivisible, they tended in actuality to be divided only with extreme difficulty.

The members of the Newcastle Circle readily seized upon the systems of both Gassend and Descartes and adapted them to their own views. There was a wide spectrum of 'atomism' within the Newcastle Circle from the neo-Aristotelianism of Kenelm Digby to the partisan Epicureanism of Margaret Cavendish, Marchioness (later Duchess) of Newcastle. The earlier Newcastle Circle of the 1630s grew larger and, looking back, more illustrious, after its removal to Paris in the 1640s. The nucleus of the group was still Hobbes, the brothers Cavendish, and Pell. Gone were Walter Warner and Robert Payne. Added were Margaret Cavendish, wife of William, William Petty, and through Hobbes, Sir Kenelm Digby, who wrote adulatory letters to Margaret.[3] This English circle was closely associated with that of Père Mersenne and Père Gassend. William Petty, in 1674, wrote of the excitement and activity of the days in Paris when there existed an unofficial 'university' of the mechanical philosophy centring around Mersenne, Gassend, Descartes, Roberval, and Hobbes:

[Y]our Grace [William Cavendish, Duke of Newcastle] doth not onely love the search of Truth, but did Encourage Me 30 years ago as to Enquiries of this kind.

[1] Gassend, *Animadversiones*, I, 725–8.

[2] See E. J. Dijksterhuis, *Mechanization of the World-Picture* (Oxford, 1961), p. 417. Henceforth cited as *Mechanization*.

[3] Douglas Grant, *Margaret the First* (London, 1957), p. 221. See also R. T. Petersson, *Sir Kenelm Digby* (Cambridge, Mass., 1956), *passim*.

For about that time in Paris, Mersennus, Gassendy, Mr. Hobs, Monsieur Des Cartes, Monsieur Roberval, Monsieur Mydorg eand other famous men, all frequenting and caressed by your Grace and your memorable brother Sir Charles Cavendish, did countenance and influence my studies as well by their Conversation as their Publick Lectures and Writings.[1]

As we have seen, Hobbes was at this time particularly close to Gassend and rather cool towards Descartes. Charles Cavendish was, on the other hand, an admirer of both mechanical philosophers; he highly esteemed Descartes' *Principia Philosophiae*.[2] He reported to Pell in 1644 that he was 'extreamlie taken with Des Cartes his new booke',[3] and yet he remained close to Gassend and valued his opinions.[4]

William Petty, later to become the virtuoso *par excellence*, during the 1640s became connected with the Newcastle Circle through his friend, John Pell. Pell introduced him to Hobbes, the Marquis of Newcastle, Sir Charles, and through them, to Mersenne, Descartes, Gassend, and other Paris savants. Petty's original interests were in mathematics, but under the tutelage of Hobbes and the others, he soon turned to physics. He was engaged by Hobbes in drawing diagrams for Hobbes' treatise on optics.[5]

In 1674, in a discourse presented to the Royal Society, Petty delineated his mechanical philosophy, which doubtless reflected very closely his interests of the 1640s.[6] The work demonstrates an ambitious, eclectic mechanical philosophy, synthesizing ideas from Gassend, Descartes, Hobbes, and Gilbert.

Petty began his discourse by supposing that the *prima materia* of the universe exists in the form of hard atoms, immutable in magnitude and figure. These atoms, through their motions, join to form corpuscles or concretions, the magnitude, motion, and form of which account for all secondary qualities. Thus far, except for conspicuously omitting mention of void of plenum, Petty's atomism is that of Gassend. However, all Petty's atoms are tiny magnets.

[E]very Atom is like the Earths Globe or Magnet, wherein are three Points considerable, viz. two in surface called Poles and one within the substance called Centre or rather Byas.[7]

Since both the heavens and the earth have these three points (two poles and a centre of gravity) the atom is a true microcosm.

[1] William Petty, *Discourse made before the Royal Society . . . Concerning the Use of Duplicate Proportion . . . together with a New Hypothesis of Springy or Elastique Motion* (London, 1674), epistle dedicatory, sig. A8v–A9v. Henceforth cited as *Discourse*.
[2] Cavendish to Pell, 10 Dec. 1644, in Halliwell, *Collections*, pp. 86–87.
[3] Cavendish to Pell, 7 September, 1644, in Halliwell, *Collections*, p. 84.
[4] Cavendish to Pell, 12 October, 1644, in Vaughan, II, pp. 371–2.
[5] Aubrey, *Lives*, p. 140.
[6] See R. Kargon, 'William Petty's Mechanical Philosophy', to appear in *Isis*.
[7] Petty, *Discourse*, p. 126.

The little atomic magnets have the same motions which Copernicus ascribed to the earth. These motions are compounded in the corpuscles. Out of the corpuscles, in turn, are compounded the physical qualities of gross bodies. The atoms have several varieties of size and shape, although those of each individual atom are immutable. The corpuscles are subject to alteration by the changed motions of the separate atoms.[1]

According to Petty, an atom rotates about its own axis, and about other atoms 'as the Moon does about the Earth; Venus and Mercury about the Sun, etc.' The centre or 'Byas' of nearby atoms attract each other.

I suppose that the Byas of one Atome may have a tendency towards the Byas of another near it.[2]

Besides this interatomic attraction, all atoms are drawn to the centre of the earth by gravity, and are affected by the earth's magnetic poles.

I suppose that all Atoms have, like a Magnet, two motions, one of Gravity whereby it tendeth towards the Centre of the Earth, and the other of Verticity by which it tendeth towards the Earths Poles.[3]

The velocities of atoms, Petty held, have different magnitudes and directions. By opposing each other, the atomic velocities can give the appearance of rest, although like Hobbes in 1645, Petty held that there is no rest in nature.[4] The probable influence of Hobbes is not surprising in view of the close contacts between Petty and Hobbes during the formative years of Petty's mechanical philosophy. Petty's view of matter is straightforward and closely dependent upon his mentors. Another natural philosopher closely associated with the Newcastle group, Kenelm Digby, has a startingly different orientation.[5]

During the 1640s, Digby was in close touch with members of Newcastle Circle, as well as having his own intercourse with Descartes, Hobbes, and others.[6] By his contemporaries, Digby was viewed as an atomist, but a reading of his treatise *Of Bodies* (1st edition, 1644), reveals a purpose differing greatly from that of his friends.[7]

Digby was, in essence, an Aristotelian who incorporated some of the views of Descartes, Gilbert, and Nicolo Cabeo into his work. Like the other 'new' philosophers of the seventeenth century, Digby virulently

---

[1] Petty, *Discourse,* p. 125.   [2] Ibid., p. 127.
[3] Ibid., p. 128.   [4] Ibid., p. 130.
[5] Kenelm Digby (1603–65) was tutored by Thomas Allen, a member of the Northumberland group. Digby was highly esteemed by contemporaries as a writer and philosopher.
[6] See Grant, pp. 93, 149, 221, 239; see also Peterson, p. 123.
[7] See, for example, Hobbes, *Works,* VII, pp. 340–1.

attacked the Schoolmen of his day. He contemptuously deprecated the scholastics when he held to be degraders of philosophy.[1] What he wished to accomplish was to revive the pristine purity of Aristotle, and demonstrate the links between him and the new philosophy.

Digby began his treatise *Of Bodies* with an attempt to define *quantity*, for 'among those primary affections which occur in the perusal of a Body, *Quantity* . . . is one, and in a manner, the first and root of all the rest.'[2] There are, Digby held, several species of *quantity*: 'Magnitude, Place, Motion, Time, Number, and Weight', but of these, magnitude and place are 'permanent'.[3] Like Descartes and Aristotle, Digby admitted no vacuum into his system; his arguments on this matter were similar to those of the Stagirite.[4]

Since a 'Body is made and constituted a Body by Quantity', a classification can be made of extended substances into *rare* and *dense* bodies. Rare and dense bodies differ only by having more or less quantity. The addition of *gravity* to this classification leads to two binary combinations; this is the origin of the four elements. Rare substances can be divided into those extremely hot and moderately dry (fire), on the one hand, and extremely humid and moderately hot, on the other (air). Dense bodies can be divided into those extremely cold and moderately wet (water), and those extremely dry and moderately cold (earth).[5]

The manner in which gravity effects this differentiation is as follows. If in a dense body the gravity 'overcomes' the density and 'breaks' it, it draws the denseness to the centre; this, according to Digby is *moistness*.[6] If, on the contrary, the density 'overcomes' the gravity, *dryness* results. Similarly, in rare bodies, if the rareness overcomes the gravity, dryness results, and if the reverse is true, moistness appears.

For Digby, the four elements are, however, made of atoms. These atoms are actually, to be sure, the '*minima naturalia*' or '*parva naturalia*' of scholastic-Averroist tradition, rather than the atoms of Democritus or Epicurus. Digby was quite specific on this point; he consciously placed himself in the Aristotelian tradition.[7]

The '*minima naturalia*' tradition has a long and quite distinguished history. Basing themselves on certain of Aristotle's texts,[8] Greek commentators such as Simplicius and Alexander of Aphrodisias and medieval commentators such as Averroes, Albertus Magnus, St. Thomas, and Augustine Nifo arrived at a theory of matter, depending upon minimum parts of

---

[1] Kenelm Digby, *Two Treatises: Of Bodies and of Man's Soul* (London, 1669). Henceforth cited as *Bodies*.

[2] Ibid., p. 9.
[3] Ibid., p. 18.
[4] Ibid., p. 25.
[5] Ibid., pp. 37–38.
[6] Ibid., p. 33.
[7] Ibid., p. 435.
[8] Particularly the *Physics*, I, 4; 187b, 18–34.

6

tangible bodies.[1] These ideas were picked up and adapted later by such thinkers as Julius Scaliger (1484–1558) to whom Digby was, in spirit, close.[2]

Scholastic *minima* and the atoms of the seventeenth-century atomists differ in several important respects. The *minima* of different substances are qualitatively different from one another, whereas atoms can differ only in size, shape and motion. In the theory of *minima*, the property of *shape* is of no importance, whereas in the seventeenth-century formulations of atomism, shape is often crucial to the production of physical qualities. Finally, in the atomic doctrine all change in nature and all qualities derive from alterations in the motions and configurations of concretions of atoms, whereas in the *minima* theory, *minima* can act upon each other to produce internal qualitative alterations.[3] In sum, the atomic theory admits of only matter in motion and mechanical interaction, but the *minima* doctrine permits interactions of a distinctly occult nature.

Digby was one of the last in a long line of Aristotelian minimists. He tried, successfully (for his own time, if not for ours), to incorporate the new ideas of Descartes, Gassend, Gilbert, and others into the larger framework of Aristotelianism. Hence, beginning with a definition of quantity, he worked back through the Aristotelian four elements to the scholastic *minima*. Finally, using the *minima* in a fashion somewhat resembling that of the new philosophers, he hoped that the gap between Aristotle and the new philosophy would be bridged. For example, Digby explained gravity,[4] odours, colours, and the efficacy of a loadstone to draw iron,[5] by the action of atomic effluvia just as did the new philosophers. Electrical attraction, according to Digby, is the result of material steams which couple.[6] Fire is composed of small atoms, the smallest bodies to be found in nature.[7] Their smallness, exility, and rapidity of motion account for the great efficacy of fire particles in working changes in nature. By a circuitous route, therefore, Digby reached a position which was neither purely mechanical nor anti-mechanical, neither 'modern' nor medieval.

The great reputation which Digby enjoyed among those engaged in the establishment of the mechanical philosophy (Hobbes, Boyle, Descartes, Charleton, etc.) is difficult to explain. He was taken to be a partisan of the new philosophy by most of his contemporaries. Sir Charles Cavendish for instance wrote that *Of Bodies* 'appears to me to have some things in it

[1] Andrew van Melsen, *From Atomos to Atom* (New York, 1960), pp. 46–48; 58–73.
[2] Ibid., pp. 73–77.
[3] Diksterhuis, *Mechanization*, p. 205.   [4] Digby, *Bodies*, p. 58.
[5] Ibid., pp. 187–230.   [6] Ibid., p. 214.
[7] Ibid., pp. 145–6.

extraordinary'.[1] Despite the fact that his book is now viewed as a strange *mélange* quite out of step with seventeenth-century developments, Digby was an important figure in the establishment of atomism in England. His books were read with interest and admiration, and, as a member of the Royal Society, his personal contributions to atomism may have been quite out of proportion to the worth of his publications.

The last figure of the Newcastle Circle to be discussed is Margaret Cavendish, the 'mad Duchess'. Margaret is best known today in the history of science for her characteristically colourful visit to the Royal Society in May 1667, so candidly described by Pepys.[2] In literary history, she is best known as a poetess, biographer, and playwright. Margaret also played, however, an interesting role in the establishment of atomism in England which has been largely overlooked, in part because it is difficult for the modern historian to take her seriously. Still, it should not be forgotten that she was a correspondent or patroness of many important figures in the history of science, including Constantijn Huygens, Walter Charleton, Kenelm Digby, Thomas Hobbes, John Evelyn, Joseph Glanvill, and Henry More. Margaret wrote copiously on natural philosophy, and her books were widely distributed in the two decades following 1650.[3]

The Newcastle Circle dispersed in the late 1640s, most of the members (including Petty, Digby, and Hobbes) returning to England. Margaret and her brother-in-law Sir Charles returned to England in 1651, where they remained until his death in 1654. During these years, Lady Margaret found time to publish two volumes of verse, *Poems and Fancies* (1653) and *Philosophical Fancies* (1653), in which she expounded an Epicurean atomism at once so extreme and so fanciful that she shocked the enemies of atomism, and embarrassed its friends.

According to Lady Margaret, atoms by their own motion may form a world.

> Small *Atomes* of themselves a *World* may make,
> As being subtle, and of every shape
> And as they dance about, fit places finde
> Such *Formes* as best agree make every kinde . . .
> So *Atomes*, as they dance, find places fit
> They there remaine, lye close, and fast will sticke.[4]

[1] Cavendish to Pell, 26 March 1645, in Vaughan, II, 361–2.
[2] Samuel Pepys, *Diary*, ed. H. B. Wheatley (London, 1893–98), VI, pp. 323–4; Thomas Birch, *History of the Royal Society* (London, 1756), II, pp. 175–8. See also S. Mintz, 'Duchess of Newcastle's Visit to the Royal Society', *Journal of English and German Philology* 51 (1952) 168–76.
[3] A check-list of her works can be found in Grant, pp. 240–2.
[4] Margaret Cavendish *Poems and Fancies* (London, 1653), p. 5. Henceforth cited as *Poems.*

These atoms exist in a vacuum, she claimed, and at least some are hollow, containing void within them.[1] Gross bodies are composed of atoms, and all change in nature arises from the altered configurations of atoms through motion.

> If *Atomes* all are of the selfe same *Matter*;
> As *Fire, Aire, Earth,* and *Water,*
> Then must their severall *Figures* make all *Change*
> By *Motions* helpe, which orders as they range.[2]

The study of motion, Lady Margaret held, is the prime investigation for a natural philosopher; had only Aristotle studied *motion* as he did *parts,* he would have been wiser.[3]

All atoms in her system have the same quantity of matter, but differ in size and shape.[4] There are four principal types of atoms, corresponding to the four elements: square, round, long, and sharp. Air atoms are long and straight, but are hollow and therefore soft. Air is able to diffuse itself over great spaces because the atoms of air can form webs or long threads of atoms, end on end.[5]

Fire atoms are sharp, mobile, and light, causing the sensation of heat through their pointedness.[6] A flame is composed of corpuscles compounded of one air atom and one fire atom, joined together.[7] Cold atoms are also sharp, light, and mobile. Round or flat atoms never freeze or burn.[8] Water atoms are round, light and hollow, accounting for its 'softness' and fluidity. Earth atoms are flat, heavy, dull, and slow.

The earth, like the sun, attracts other bodies through the exhalation of sharp atoms.

> The reason *Earth* attracts much like the *Sun*
> Is, *Atomes sharpe* out from the Earth do come . . .
> And as they wander meet with duller *Formes,*
> Wherein they sticke their *point* & then back *returnes.*[9]

Psychological as well as physical phenomena have their origin in atomic motion. The operations of the mind are nothing but the local motion of vapours in the brain.[10] This, of course, is a doctrine closely resembling that which Hobbes taught Lady Margaret's husband as early as 1630. Memory, according to Lady Margaret's doctrine, 'is Atomes in the Brain set on fire'.[11]

---

[1] Margaret Cavendish, *Poems,* pp. 20–21.
[2] Ibid., p. 10. See also Margaret Cavendish, *Natures Pictures Drawn by Fancies Pencil to the Life* (London, 1656), p. 297. Henceforth cited as *Pictures.*
[3] Ibid., pp. 400–1.   [4] Margaret Cavendish, *Poems,* p. 8.
[5] Ibid., pp. 6–7.   [6] Ibid., p. 6.
[7] Ibid., p. 11.   [8] Ibid., p. 13.
[9] Ibid., p. 21.   [10] Margaret Cavendish, *Pictures,* p. 178.
[11] Ibid., p. 130.

A large section of the *Poems and Fancies* is devoted to the medical implications of the atomic theory. It is possible that Lady Margaret became interested in this subject through her friend, Walter Charleton, a physician, later F.R.S. and F.R.C.P., an avowed atomist who translated her biography of William Cavendish into Latin in 1668. It is equally possible, and quite likely, that Margaret arrived at these charming speculations without help.

According to Lady Margaret, disease is caused by the 'fighting' of atoms,[1] and by the effect of the congelation of atoms upon the fluid balance of the body. For example, an excess of round atoms (water) when they congeal, causes dropsy. Sharp atoms, causing heat and dryness, result in consumption. When the body has an over-abundance of long air corpuscles, the body will suffer from too much wind or 'collick'. Flat, slow atoms stop up body passages causing palsy or apoplexy.[2]

Lady Margaret did not fear to tread upon dangerous ground. The mere fact of her atomism was enough to cause concern in some circles; that she admitted that atoms, *of themselves*, could make a world was near heresy. She compounded her seeming apostasy by adhering to very unorthodox ideas about the soul and about atheism. Like the ancient atomists (and Hobbes), Margaret held that the soul is corporeal, albeit rare and pure.

The Soul [she wrote] is a substance, yet such a substance as to be the Rarest and Purest substance in nature, which makes it so apt to ascend, as to make the Brain the Residing place; it is the Celestial Part of Man, whereas the Body is but the terrestrial part.[3]

That the soul is incorporeal and therefore 'nothing' she laughed at as 'absurd'.[4]

Lady Margaret evinced a tenderness towards atheism which was dangerous for one so closely tied to the suspect atomic philosophy.

It is better to be an atheist [she wrote in 1650] than a superstitious man; for in Atheisme there is humanitie, and civility towards man to man; but superstition regards no humanity, but begets cruelty to all things, even to themselves.[5]

It is no wonder, then, that she presented a problem to the defenders of atomism. Her own version of Epicurean atomism was fanciful and of little use to the natural philosophers. For this she was actually reproached (but gently) by her friend, Charleton.[6] More importantly, she obviously laid the atomists open to attack on the charge of impiety, a charge made more

[1] Margaret Cavendish, *Poems,* p. 15.
[2] Ibid., p. 15.
[3] Margaret Cavendish, *Orations of Divers Sorts* (London, 1662), p. 304.
[4] Ibid., pp. 308–09.
[5] Margaret Cavendish, *Worlds Olio* (London, 1655), p. 45. This was written in 1650.
[6] Grant, p. 222.

serious by the 'excesses' of Hobbes. In order to 'purify' atomism, the friends of Hobbes and Lady Margaret were required to dissociate themselves from their views and assure the pious that atomism could in fact be rid of its atheistic implications. It was to this task that Walter Charleton, John Evelyn, Robert Boyle, and others devoted themselves in the 1650s.

VIII

WALTER CHARLETON
AND THE ACCEPTANCE
OF ATOMISM IN ENGLAND

THE appearance in 1649 of Gassend's *Animadversiones in decimum librum Diogenis Laertii* and the small *Epicuri Philosophiae Syntagma* appended to it provided amenable natural philosophers with a complete system of physics, rivalled only by that of Descartes. Gassend's book was eagerly awaited by those interested in the new philosophy, and became an instantaneous success.[1] Copies of the first printing sold out quickly in Paris, and were difficult to obtain even on the continent.[2] It is doubtless for this reason that Gassend's direct impact was greatest within the range of his personal contact; in England where in the 1650s his books were less readily available, knowledge of his ideas and their importance came largely through the mediation of the Newcastle Circle and Gassend's great friend Hobbes.

Soon after the appearance of the *Animadversiones,* the Newcastle Circle began to dissolve, and members drifted quietly back to England. Lady Margaret of Newcastle began to publish her poetry and to collect around her a faithful group of admirers. Hobbes, too, acquired a large circle of friends, despite (or perhaps because of) the notoriety engendered by the publication of the *Leviathan* in 1651.

Included in the entourage of the transplanted Newcastle Circle were the physician, Walter Charleton, the poet Edmund Waller, John Evelyn, and numerous others. After the restoration, William Cavendish became Duke of Newcastle, and Lady Margaret, as Duchess, became an important social and literary figure. A collection of letters published in 1676 clearly delineates her wide connections.[3] The contributors included Charleton, Evelyn, Constantijn Huygens, Kenelm Digby, Joseph Glanvill, and Hobbes. It was in this colourful and influential group around Hobbes and the Duchess that Gassend's atomism first was introduced and took root. Hobbes himself, as

[1] Pell to Charles Cavendish, 16 May 1649, in Helen Hervey, 'Hobbes and Descartes in the Light of Some Correspondence between Sir Charles Cavendish and Dr. John Pell', *Osiris* **10** (1952) 87.

[2] Ibid., pp. 87–88.

[3] *Letters and Poems in Honour of the Incomparable Princess, Margaret, Dutchess of Newcastle* (London, 1676).

we have seen, came to differ widely from his French friend, yet without doubt recognized the latter's abilities and discussed them with his acquaintances. The reception of Cartesianism in England has been the subject of several excellent studies,[1] but the reception of atomism has unfortunately been neglected. It will be the purpose of this chapter to sketch this early reception, and examine the problems which it raised.

Despite the importance of the mediation of the returning *emigrés* for the acceptance of Gassend's atomism, it would be absurd to insist that there existed no independent interest in his atomism in England. Direct knowledge of the *Animadversiones* and the *Syntagma* certainly existed, and was not unimportant. Gassend's system, like that of Descartes, was widely discussed at the universities in the early 1650s. Among those interested in the problems presented by the new mechanical philosophies was Newton's teacher, Isaac Barrow. In 1652, he defended the thesis '*Cartesiana Hypothesis de Materia et Motu haud satisfacit praecipuis Naturae Phenomenis*'. This lecture, reprinted in Barrow's *Theological Works,* is an interesting and extremely important document, apparently overlooked by the historians of Cartesianism in England.[2] The work clearly demonstrates the inroads which the mechanical philosophy had made at Cambridge by 1652, and the problems which it continued to face.

Barrow opened his discourse with a kind word for Greek natural philosophers including Anaxagoras, Aristotle, Plato, Epicurus, and Democritus; he deplored the post-Aristotelian neglect of natural philosophy. Recently, Barrow continued, natural philosophy has begun to revive; Magnenus, Gassend, Digby, Gilbert, and others have renewed ancient systems and struck out upon new paths. But among the new philosophers, the best known is Descartes, an 'ingenious and important philosopher'.[3] But Descartes, so far from being infallible, can be controverted on many points; to this end Barrow cited Plato, Aristotle, 'Democritus or Epicurus', the Chemists, natural magicians, and, *above all,* Bacon.[4]

Plato and Aristotle, Barrow wrote, would have condemned the Cartesian habit of ignoring the spiritual and immaterial—those substances which form and guide the development of the world. How have plants, for

[1] Marjorie Nicolson, 'Early Stage of Cartesianism in England', *Studies in Philology* **26** (1929) 451–74; Sterling Lamprecht, 'Role of Descartes in Seventeenth Century England', *Studies in the History of Ideas* (New York, 1935), III, pp. 181–242; J. E. Saveson, 'Differing Reactions to Descartes among the Cambridge Platonists', *J. Hist. Ideas* **21** (1960) 560–7; Saveson, 'Descartes' Influence on John Smith, Cambridge Platonist', *J. Hist. Ideas* **20** (1959) 259–73; Danton Sailor, 'Cudworth and Descartes', *J. Hist. Ideas* **23** (1962) 133–40.
[2] Isaac Barrow, *Theological Works,* ed. Alexander Napier (Cambridge, 1859), IX, 79. Henceforth cited as *Works.*
[3] Ibid., IX, 79–81.
[4] Ibid., IX, 86. Emphasis supplied.

example, attained their beauty and healing virtues, if not by expressed Providence, acting through an inward spirit?[1] Moreover, Democritus Epicurus, and Hero of Alexandria have demonstrated the existence of the void. As Lucretius put it, without void nothing could be moved, for it is the nature of body to resist motion. In a plenum, body is everywhere, and motion nowhere.[2] The Cartesian hypothesis, Barrow concluded, cannot satisfy all phenomena in nature.[3]

The little address by Barrow is more important for its implications than its content. It demonstrates, in the first place, that Cartesianism was a live issue at Cambridge by 1652, though probably frowned upon officially. Barrow's tutor, Duport, is known to have been vehemently anti-mechanist.[4] Moreover, the names of Gassend and Digby were sufficiently well known to require, when mentioned, no further explication. Gassend's 'purification' of atomism had been successful enough to permit Barrow to use the ancient atomists to attack Descartes. Finally, Barrow raised some of the important theological points which were to trouble the reception of the atomic philosophy in England, primarily those involving the role of Providence. It would be well, also, to keep in mind these two important points: Barrow's reliance upon Bacon and the atomists to refute Descartes, and the concern for the inclusion of immaterial causes in natural philosophy. These points reappear in the early manuscripts of Isaac Newton, and it is quite likely that Newton's interests were guided by those of his mentor, Barrow.

The reverence which Barrow accorded Bacon is extremely interesting. In the 1650s, there appears to have been a revival of Francis Bacon's reputation as a natural philosopher. Barrow was particularly concerned with Baconian method; he opted for Bacon's experimentalism over the rationalism of Descartes.[5] Throughout the 1650s and 1660s the importance of Bacon as promulgator of a new method increased. There was, however, no consensus regarding the exact nature of this method. Some, like Boyle, attempted to use experiment to illustrate the theories of his contemporaries; it was his duty, he held, to show wherein the theories of the Cartesians and the atomists were consonant with experience. For others, like Newton, experiment was a way to *certainty*, a new organon for transforming physics from the realm of hypothesis to the realm of precision.[6] It was this latter stream of Baconianism, combining experiment and the mechanical philosophy in a new way, which began in England with Barrow and reached its high-water mark with the work of Newton.

[1] Ibid., IX, 93–96.　　　　　[2] Ibid., IX, 99.
[3] Ibid., IX, 102.
[4] Percy Osmond, *Isaac Barrow, his life and times* (London, 1944), p. 28.
[5] Barrow, *Works,* IX, 97–104.　　　　[6] See below, Chapter X.

Another example of the direct influence of Gassend upon English thought was the work of the minor Jesuit polemicist, Guy Holland. His *Grand Prerogative of Humane Nature,* which appeared in 1653, is in most respects a standard of defense of the immortality and immateriality of the soul.[1] In it, he attacked Volkelius, the Socinian, Thomas Browne, and, of course, Hobbes.[2] Holland spoke well of the purifying influence of Gassend, who 'refutes' Lucretius to the advantage of atomism.[3] In the same year that Holland's little work appeared, the reception of atomism was given important reinforcement by the Gruter-Boswell edition of Bacon's early works favourable to atomism under the title *Scripta in . . . Philosophia.*[4] The reprinting of the early atomic works of Bacon may have given considerable impetus to the acceptance of atomism.

As atomism became better known in the 1650s, the old spectre atheism returned to haunt it. The views of Epicurus and Lucretius began to be openly and vehemently attacked with greater frequency. The obvious unorthodoxy of Hobbes and Margaret Cavendish were linked with the atomist school, and the latter was roundly condemned for the former's 'heresies', as well as for its own views.

One of the chief issues was the question of the materiality and mortality of the soul. Hobbes and Lady Margaret, it will be recalled, both insisted upon the material nature of spirits. Both denied the existence of immaterial substances—a notion which Hobbes held to be a contradiction in terms. During the 1640s this issue assumed a political immediacy as well as theological importance.

By the fifth decade of the seventeenth century, the decay of the traditional social, political, and intellectual structures in England was made strikingly apparent by the deep fissures everywhere in evidence. The period of the Civil War was accompanied, for example, by attacks upon Church and theology—upon both Puritan and High Church orthodoxies. Numerous schools of sectarians, free-thinkers, and non-conformists flourished during the troubled times. No less than sixteen heretical sects were singled out by one contemporary clergyman as 'blasphemous'.[5] In early 1646, the London municipal authorities became so appalled by the dangerously large amount of discussion supporting anti-scripturalism and quasianarchism that they requested Parliament to repress all private meetings. On 6 February 1646, a solemn fast was declared in London to denounce the increase in heresy and blasphemy. In 1648, Parliament, by a large majority, passed legislation for the suppression of heretics and

[1] Guy Holland, *Grand Prerogative of Humane Nature* (London, 1953).
[2] Ibid., pp. 119–20.   [3] Ibid., p. 25.
[4] See above, Chapter V.
[5] Thomas Edwards, *Gangraena* (London, 1646), p. 13.

blasphemers.[1] The atmosphere of the time was not one in which unorthodox thinkers could take comfort.

The cause of much, but by no means all, of the apprehension was the activity of the Levellers, a democratic political party which advocated government by law, popular sovereignty, equality under the law, and a popular military. In religious matters, the Levellers demanded freedom of conscience and participation only by consent.[2] Among the 'heresies' advocated by a major Leveller writer was one which maintained 'that the soul dies with the body and all things shall have an end'.[3] This particular heresy was the subject of a tract published in 1643 by Richard Overton, a founder of the Leveller party, and a close associate of General Lilburne. The work, *Mans Mortallitie,* is a straightforward denial of the immateriality and immortality of the soul. Overton was concerned with proving that man is composed of wholly mortal components.[4] The common distinction between body and soul, or matter and spirit, Overton wrote, is false. The soul, he held, is merely an expression of the body, and perishes with it. Everything which is created, he held, is material, and that which is not material cannot be said to exist. What has been termed a 'soul' is merely a collection of faculties.[5]

As a thinly veiled attack upon organized religion, its institutions, and its exponents, Overton's pamphlet rapidly achieved great notoriety. It was reprinted in new editions of 1644, 1655, and 1675.[6] Overton's tract is important to atomism in this regard: it posed publicly and forcefully the question of the respectability of a materialist conception of the universe, and thereby became the lightning rod for criticism of Epicureanism, although it was not itself, strictly speaking, an Epicurean tract. The magnitude of Overton's notoriety, based upon this pamphlet and upon his political activities, created the necessity for the English followers of Gassend to distinguish themselves from him, and from the 'mortalist' position.[7]

The outcry against Overton's pamphlet was vigorous. On 26 August 1644, in view of the response to *Mans Mortallitie,* the House of Commons ordered an investigation of publishers of pamphlets against the immortality of the soul. But the concern with the spread of these potentially dangerous

[1] John Roberts, *Short History of Freethought* (London, 1906), II, 92.
[2] Anonymous, *The Leveller* (London, 1659) in *Harleian Miscellany* (London, 1809), IV, 543.
[3] Edwards, p. 17.
[4] Richard Overton, *Mans Mortallitie* (Amsterdam, 1643), *passim.* See also Denis Saurat, *Milton et le matérialisme chrétien en Angleterre* (Paris, 1928), p. 48.
[5] Overton, pp. 9–17, 54. See also Wilber Jordan, *Development of Religious Toleration in England* (Cambridge, Mass., 1932–40). IV, 191.
[6] Saurat, p. 47.
[7] An excellent discussion of the 'mortalist' controversy can be found in George Williamson, 'Milton and the Mortalist Heresy', *Studies in Philology* 32 (1935) 553–79.

ideas was not confined to religious enthusiasts, polemicists, and Parliament. Epicureanism was the spectre which haunted the theological and literary circles at Oxford and Cambridge as well. At Emmanuel College, Cambridge, Epicureanism was most systematically attacked. At Emmanuel, men committed to a more tolerant religious attitude, the 'Cambridge Platonists', addressed themselves to the dangers to Christianity of the Epicurean doctrine.

The first systematic attack upon the Epicureans was made by John Smith, a Cambridge Platonist. Smith's assaults, first presented to the Cambridge community in the form of lectures, discussions, and sermons in the 1640s and early 1650s, were published posthumously in 1660.[1] Smith's essays show that he had a first-hand knowledge of the Epicureanism current in intellectual circles, and moreover, by their sense of urgency, demonstrate that the heretical views were far more popular than it was safe to permit. Smith's *Discourse Demonstrating the Immortality of the Soul* was written during the mid-1640s. In it, Smith attacked a certain 'Greek Philosopher' and his followers who call the soul 'Material and Divisible, though of a fine aethereal nature'.[2] By a reduction to absurdity, Smith attempted to disprove the Epicurean contention that the soul is composed of atoms:

A man's new-born Soul will for all this be but little better than his Body; and, as that is, be but a *rasura corporis alieni*, made up of some small and thin shavings pared off from the Bodies of the Parents by a continuall motion of the several parts of it.[3]

Then, absurdly,

The very Grass we walk over in the fields . . . may according to the true meaning of this dull philosophy, after many refinings . . . which Nature performs by the help of Motion, spring up into so many Rational Souls and prove as wise as any Epicurean.[4]

Smith's tract, *A Short Discourse of Atheism,* attacked with so great a gusto that it could leave an Epicurean no choice but to reply. The doctrine is immediately denounced as blasphemous: 'Epicurism is but Atheism under a Mask.'[5] Throughout the discourse, Smith unsympathetically presented some physical doctrine of the Epicureans, and contended that they are not only blasphemous but also ridiculous.[6] One doctrine which he particularly

[1] John Smith, *Select Discourses* (London, 1660). Henceforth cited as *Discourses*.
[2] Smith, 'Discourse Demonstrating the Immortality of the Soul', in E. T. Campagnac, *Cambridge Platonists* (Oxford, 1901), p. 106.
[3] Campagnac, p. 111.
[4] Ibid.
[5] Smith, *Discourses,* p. 41.
[6] Ibid., pp. 46–47.

singled out is the idea that the power of motion is inherent in matter. Even granting this atheistic notion will not, however, render the system plausible.

> And yet could we allow Epicurus this power of Motion to be feated in Nature yet that he might perform the true task of a Naturalist he must also give us an account how such a force and power in Nature should subsist, which is easy to doe; if we call in . . . God himself as the Architect and Mover of this Divine Artifice; but without some infinite power is impossible.[1]

Smith's arguments, although not published until 1660, were familiar ones by the early 1650s; the points which he raised concerning the nature of the soul, and the inherency of motion in matter became standard objections to Epicurean atomism. Henry More, another Cambridge Platonist, continued these attacks, and popularized them.

In 1653, More published the first edition of his *Antidote Against Atheism* in which he, too, entered the spirit-matter controversy, sharpened by the publication of the *Leviathan* in 1651. *Contra* Hobbes, More was concerned with upholding the existence of incorporeal substances in the universe. The soul, More maintained, is not a mere modification of the body, but the source of activity in nature. His argument rested, in part, upon the incapability of self-motion by matter. It is God, he held, who ultimately actuates all corporeal substances. The soul of man is not corporeal, but an incorporeal, self-moving spiritous substance.[2] More insisted upon the necessity of including these spirits in the philosophy of nature. Even the celebrated phenomenon of gravity is not, as the mechanical philosophers would have it, the result of the mere motion of material particles, but rather of an *immaterial* cause.

> But . . . the Phaenomenon of Gravity is quite cross and contrary to the very first *Mechanick laws of Motion* which yet is an Universal law of Terrestrial bodies put upon them by that which is not onely not Terrestrial, but Immaterial.[3]

In these matters, More attacked 'our profound *Atheists* and *Epicureans*' who, according to More, adhered to the pagan hypothesis of the fortuitous dance of atoms.[4] All nature, More held, loudly proclaims the presence of divine providence.

The year 1653 was a critical one for Epicurean atomism. The attacks of its opponents were more frequent than before. Hobbes' *Leviathan* (1651) and Margaret Cavendish's two volumes of 1653 provided an extreme from which more pious atomists had to dissociate themselves. The initiative was assumed by Walter Charleton (1619–1707), an early disciple of Gassend,

[1] Smith, *Discourses*, p. 48.
[2] Henry More, *Collection of Several Philosophical Writings* (London, 1662), pp. 32–36.
[3] Ibid., p. 46.   [4] Ibid., p. 47.

who took the first systematic steps to purify atomism. Charleton's *Physiologia Epicuro-Gassendo-Charltoniana*, a translation and expansion of the long section on physics of Gassend's *Animadversiones*, was the first work of natural philosophy which seriously attacked this problem. Other English works had previously dealt with the subject of atoms, but none treated the subject in so comprehensive a fashion.[1]

A friend of Hobbes and a correspondent of Lady Margaret Cavendish, Charleton probably first came into contact with the ideas of Gassend through them. At any rate, shortly after their return to England, Charleton abandoned his earlier adherence to the ideas of Van Helmont and became an enthusiastic atomist.

Charleton was educated at Magdalen Hall (later Hertford College), Oxford, at which he matriculated in July 1635.[2] In January 1643, he was appointed physician-in-ordinary to Charles I, a position which he retained until 1649.[3] Charleton remained an ardent Royalist; his publications during the Commonwealth proudly recall his position as physician to the late King. The Royal Society elected him to fellowship in 1663,[4] and the Royal College of Physicians chose him as an honorary fellow in 1664, an ordinary fellow in 1676, and president, 1689–91.

One of Charleton's outstanding personal characteristics was his piety. The attacks upon Epicurean principles by men of academic and theological stature were difficult enough for him to bear in silence, but the attempts to place all Epicurean atomists in the same blasphemous company was too much for his restraint. He knew that a reply to the attacks was necessary; the Epicurean atomism to which he himself adhered, that of Gassend, was not only philosophically sound, but theologically purified.

Charleton was faced with several difficult problems. Atomism was linked with unorthodoxy, not only through its pagan origins, but also through the unorthodoxy of Hobbes and Lady Margaret who were associated with it. Gassend, it is true, made an excellent beginning in ridding atomism of its atheistical taint. But the continued assault on atomism required a new and more clearly defined defense. The *Biographia Britannica* reports that Charleton himself was attacked for his views, and was reportedly scorned by some as a Hobbist.[5] It was the impact of such criticism which began Charleton's extended defense of the atomic philosophy.

[1] Others were Thomas Browne's *Pseudodoxia Epidemica* (1648), Robert Burton's *Anatomy of Melancholy* (1621), a translation of a work of Comenius under the title *Naturall Philosophie Reformed by Divine Light* (1651), and, of course, Nicholas Hill's *Philosophia Epicurea* (1601).

[2] Wood, *Athenae Oxonienses*, IV, 752.

[3] Humphrey Rolleston, 'Walter Charleton, D.M., F.R.C.P., F.R.S.', *Bull. Hist. Med.* 8 (1940) 403.

[4] Thomas Birch, *History of the Royal Society of London* (London, 1756), I, 239.

[5] *Biographia Britannica,* 2nd ed. (London, 1778–93), III, 445.

Charleton set about to defend his atomism cleverly and effectively. His approach was threefold. First, Charleton would try to demonstrate that the modern Epicureanism of Gassend was purged of the heresies which admittedly contaminated the pagan formulations, specifically that the soul is material and mortal, and that motion is inherent in matter. Secondly, he would try to dissociate atomism from the strictly materialist views of Hobbes, Lady Margaret Cavendish, and such vulgar heretics as Overton *by joining the assault.* Thirdly, he would show how powerful the atomic doctrine can be in *promoting* piety, a notion first broached by Bacon forty years earlier. These defenses formed the substance of his book *The Darknes of Atheism Refuted by the Light of Nature: a physico-theologicall Treatise.*[1] The method chosen by Charleton to accomplish his goals reveals a certain shrewdness. Ostensibly *Darknes* is a refutation of the uniquitous and nameless 'atheists'. Charleton very subtly placed himself (and his Epicurean atomism) on the side of the angels, and in the advertisement to the reader, he joined the attack.

England . . . hath of late produced, and doth at this unhappy day foster more swarms of Atheisticall monsters (such at least whose licentious practices and insolent Discourses in Publick do equally declare their wild Ambition to be so accounted; as if the only way to acquire the reputation of being Transcendent Wits were to seem able with bold and specious Arguments to impugne the greatest and most sacred Verities . . .) then any age, then any Nation hath been infested withall.[2]

Unlike those materialists whose notions were highly questionable, Charleton claimed not to countenance blasphemy, but on the contrary purported to hold the most docile views. Specifically, Charleton dissociated himself from the ideas that the soul is mortal and that motion is inherent in matter. To impute an inherent motion to matter is to remove the necessity for God from the universe; the Epicurean atomists were vigorously attacked for this 'error' by Smith and by More. According to Charleton, however, not only did God create the universe, but His Providence, 'the constant Conservation and Moderation' of the universe, is in evidence.

If, Charleton continued, one can argue for the existence of God on the basis of the evidence of design in the universe, how much more forceful is the proof when *atoms* are supposed.

Is it possible for anything that doth pretend to Humanity, to imagine, or by any specious argument to hope to perswade that so many minute bodies or Atoms, by the rash and undeterminate conduct of their own innate propensity to motion, could . . . meet and unite in just that number which was sufficient to make of the

[1] Walter Charleton, *Darknes of Atheism Refuted by the Light of Nature* (London, 1652). Henceforth cited as *Darknes.*
[2] Ibid., advertisement, sig. ar.

Globe of the Earth, requisite to compose to compose the body of the Sun . . . and exactly accommodate to the great body of the world whose bounds we know not and whose dimensions are immense?[1]

That such a complex and interdependent universe could evolve through mere chance was beyond the credulity of Charleton. An atomistic world could not be the result of a Godless evolution; *God* was required to supply the exact proportions.

In 1654 Charleton added to his physico-theological work a complete physical treatise, the *Physiologia Epicuro-Gassendo-Charltoniana: a Fabrick of Science Natural upon the Hypothesis of Atoms, Founded by Epicurus, Repaired by Petrus Gassendus, Augmented by Walter Charleton*.[2] The *Physiologia* is the first systematic attempt in England to present Epicurean atomism as a mechanical philosophy. The work is, in essence, an expanded translation of the section of Gassend's *Animadversiones* entitled 'Physiologia Epicuri'. Charleton stressed certain concepts required by the theological tenor of his time, in particular those demanded by the theologians, Smith and More. Moreover, he emphasized certain physical doctrines which show the influence of his friend, Hobbes.

The *Physiologia* of Charleton follows Gassend's *Animadversiones* very closely with a few additions and alterations. Like Gassend, Charleton began with two fundamental principles: the atom, or plenitude, and the void. Although he denied the existence of the Cartesian aether,[3] Charleton also dismissed the notion of a collected vacuum. Corporeal effluvia, such as light, and magnetic or electrical particles are always present in any artificially created void. The magnetic efflux of the earth, for example, pervades the most formidable shields, and foils any attempt to create a truly void space.[4] The vacuum, consequently, exists disseminated throughout the physical world.

The framework for the motion of matter is one of absolute space and time. 'The Dimensions of space . . . [Charleton wrote] we have formerly intimated to be neither Active nor Passive but to have only a general non-repugnancy or Admissive Capacity whereby it receives Bodies either permanentur or transeuntur.'[5] Similarly 'unconcerned Time [doth] flow on eternally in the same calm and equal tenor.'[6] Within this framework, the first matter exists in the form of *atoms*. All visible bodies are composed of these corporeal, indissoluble, impenetrable, and invisible corpuscles, the only essential properties of which are magnitude, figure, and motion.[7]

---

1 Charleton, *Darknes,* p. 61.
2 Walter Charleton, *Physiologia* . . . (London, 1654).
3 Ibid., pp. 40–41.
5 Ibid., p. 68.
7 Ibid., pp. 111–12.

4 Ibid., p. 42.
6 Ibid., p. 76.

The problem of motion remained a difficult one for Charleton. The doctrine of antiquity 'this faeculent doctrine of Epicurus', that atoms were eternally existent and that their motion was inherent in them, was clearly unacceptable.[1] Following Gassend, Charleton held a 'purified' position: that the atoms were created by God *ex nihilo* and were infused by God with their motive virtue or 'Internal Energy' which is the 'First Cause of all Natural Actions'.[2]

The reasons for these alterations are clear. The atheism of Epicurus and Lucretius had to be exorcized from atomism if it were to be permitted to flourish. The atomic hypothesis, thus purified, would then, according to Charleton, be the most formidable and plausible philosophy to explain physical qualities on a mechanical basis.

For by virtue of these correctives [Charleton insisted] the poisonous part of Epicurus' opinion may be converted into one of the most potent Antidotes against our Ignorance: the Quantity of Atoms sufficing to the Motivation of all Concretions and their various Figures and Motions to the Origination of their Qualities and Affections.[3]

After these small changes are made, atomism becomes a simple and palatable natural philosophy.

Once God is posited as the First Cause, all phenomena can be explained, according to Charleton, in terms of matter in motion; the emphasis upon the role of motion is unmistakable. This motion is impressed by God upon the atoms at their creation. The atoms of first matter are devoid of the secondary qualities of 'colour, sound, odour, sapour, Heat, Cold, Humidity, Siccity, Aspersity, Smoothness, Hardness, Softness, etc.[4]' These qualities are but the result of the effect of the motion and shape of the 'concretions' formed of atoms upon the various organs of sense. For example, colours arise from the way in which light particles strike the eye. Sound arises from the motion of the most subtle part of the air.[5] Odours are corporeal exhalations. Heat and cold are also exhalations; the earth itself is known to belch out both hot and cold effluvia.[6] It would be erroneous, however, to assume that certain atoms are hot or cold in themselves. These qualities are the result of the magnitude, shape, and motion of the atoms and their concretions. 'These atoms . . . be not hot essentially.'[7] They are 'calorifick' atoms only in the sense that they are 'exile in Magnitude, Spherical in Figure, most Swift in Motion', for 'Motion is the Mother of Heat'.[8] Through the motion of these heat-causing atoms, the heated body is caused to diffuse and expand, i.e. become hot.

---

[1] Charleton, *Physiologia,* p. 126.   [2] Ibid., p. 126.
[3] Ibid., p. 126.   [4] Ibid. p. 190.
[5] Ibid., p. 218.   [6] Ibid., pp. 307–10.
[7] Ibid., p. 294.   [8] Ibid., p. 211.

The atomic hypothesis can account as well for the so-called 'occult qualities'. In reality, Charleton maintained, there are no 'occult' qualities. All attractions and repulsions hitherto termed 'occult' are actually caused by material, mechanical intermediaries.[1] In fact, all physics must be governed by certain rules of natural philosophy; those which Charleton outlined are reminiscent of those of Hobbes. According to Charleton, the natural philosopher must assume:

(1) That every Effect must have its Cause.
(2) That no Cause can act but by Motion.
(3) That Nothing can act upon a Distant subject or upon such whereunto it is not actually praesent, either by itself or by some instrument . . . i.e. by the mediation of some continued organ, and that an corporeal one too, or by it self alone.[2]

All phenomena, including the abhorrence of a vacuum, electrical and magnetic attractions, and gravity, must be explained mechanically. This mode of philosophizing correlates the explanations of phenomena hitherto uncorrelated, inexplicable or explicable only by wild *ad hoc* hypothesis.

Charleton also set down, in a modest fashion, the rudiments of a mechanical chemistry. The first matter, in the form of atoms, is non-corruptible. But the concretions composed of atoms can be built up and taken apart. Gravity, or the principle of motion, is the cause of "corruption". Gold is least corruptible because its concretions are the most stable.[3] Solubility, or the "dissolution of one body by the subingress or insinuation of the particles of another, must arise from the greater subtility of the particles of the Dissolvent".[4]

Finally, Charleton returned to a treatment of *motion*, a fuller discussion of which he left for last because, he said, it is the most important. Significantly, Charleton departed from Gassend at this point. He rearranged the order of the chapters of this part in order to discuss *motion* at length at the close of the work. Moreover, in his paeans to Motion, Charleton went far beyond Gassend. In this dedication to motion, one can, perhaps, detect the influence of his friend, Hobbes.

If [Charleton wrote in the *Physiologia*] Generation, Corruption, Diminution, Alteration be only . . . the Effects of Motion, as our immediately praecedent Chapter clearly imports, and that we can have no other cognizance of the conditions or qualities of sensible objects but what results from our perception of the Impulses made upon the organs of our senses by their species thither transmitted:

---

[1] Charleton, *Physiologia*, p. 343.   [2] Ibid., p. 343.
[3] Ibid., pp. 430-2.   [4] Ibid., p. 266.

assuredly the Physiologist is highly concerned to make the contemplation of Motion, its Causes, Kinds and Universal Laws, the First Link in the Chain of all his Natural Theorems.[1]

In the atomic philosophy as Charleton presented it, *motion* doubtlessly occupies the central role. It is, as he stated, 'the First Thread . . . of our Philosophy'.[2]

Charleton's *Physiologia* is of importance as a pioneer attempt to establish atoms, according to Gassend's interpretation, as a respectable natural philosophy. Thomas Mayo's *Epicurus in England,* which is a study of Epicureanism in England after 1650, correctly portrays Charleton as the first important Epicurean of the latter seventeenth century in England.[3] Mayo neglects, however, Charleton's two major works of 1652 and 1654, and begins his analysis with Charleton's relatively minor *Epicurus' Morals* of 1656. It was the *Physiologia.* on the contrary, which was Charleton's first important attempt to establish Epicureanism. As one of the first systematic atomist works published in the English language, it was largely instrumental in popularizing atomism in the 1650s and 1660s. To Charleton must be given much of the credit for removing the stain of atheism, if merely through his boldness in publishing the system with its pious alterations.

Charleton's attempt to 'purify' atomism was in a very real sense successful. After the *Physiologia,* almost all English atomist works contained the pious alterations which he, following Gassend, included. Moreover, the *Physiologia* served one additional function for the English scientific community. It made Gassend's physics readily available to those whose Latin was weak (and these were more numerous than they admitted) and to those to whom the *Animadversiones* was not readily available. Charleton did not go unnoticed; his *Physiologia* was read by such seventeenth-century luminaries as Newton and, very probably, Boyle.[4]

To Charleton's revival of English atomism was soon added the works of some of his friends. The *De Corpore* of Hobbes appeared in 1655, and in 1656 Charleton published his *Epicurus' Morals,* a translation of Epicurean ethics to which he prefixed an *apologia* for Epicurus. The *Morals* of 1656, while of literary interest, added little or nothing to the acceptance of atomism. More important in this respect was John Evelyn's *Essay on the First Book of T.*

[1] Charleton, *Physiologia,* p. 435. [2] Ibid., p. 436.
[3] Thomas Mayo, *Epicurus in England* (Dallas, 1934), p. 33. Another excellent treatment of the influence of the ancient atomists in England, concentrating primarily on the literary influence, is Charles Harrison's 'Ancient Atomists and English Literature of the Seventeenth Century', *Harvard Studies in Classical Philology* 45 (1934) 1–79.
[4] Richard Westfall, 'The Foundations Newton's Philosophy of Nature', *Br. J. Hist. Sci.* 1 (1962) 172–3 and below, Chapters IX and X.

Lucretius Carus De Rerum Natura of that same year. Evelyn continued, after the fashion of Charleton (whom he acknowledged), to purify the atomic philosophy by revising some tainted atomist tenets. Even before the book was published Evenly was criticized by his friends for preparing an Epicurean work. Jeremy Taylor wrote to him on 16 April 1656:

> I will not say to you that your Lucretius is as far distant from the severity of a Christian as the faire Ethiopian was from the duty of Bp. Heliodorus; . . . I hope you either have by notes or will by preface prepare a sufficient antidote.[1]

To be sure, Evelyn was not going to permit pagan atheism to pass unchallenged. In his reply to Taylor he assured him that:

> My essay upon Lucretius which I told you was engaged is now printing and (as I understand) neare finished; my animadversions upon it will I hope provide against all the ill consequences, and totally acquit me either of glory or impiety.[2]

Evelyn kept his word. In the preface to the reader, Evelyn apologized for Lucretius in the following fashion:

> And if our Poet have any one passage (as where he prevaricates on *Providence*, the *Immortality of the Soul*, the spontaneous coalition of *Principles*, and some other sublime points of speculative Theologie) which seems to concern or be any whit obnoxious to our Faith; he hath a thousand more where . . . he perswades to a life most exact and *Moral*.[3]

These points of 'prevarication' are exactly those fixed upon by Charleton.

> Our *Carus*, with all his eight reasons [was] refuted by the ingenious Dr. Charlton whose discourse I suppose nothing can easily be added besides trouble to the Reader.[4]

As an atomist, however, Evelyn was not always orthodox. In a supplementary discourse, possibly under the influence of Descartes, Evelyn strayed from strict atomism.

> In the meantime [he wrote] there is a middle and more probable opinion, as some conceive, who allowing of no such *Atomes* pitch upon *Insensible parts infinitely divisible* which united with many become sensible.[5]

---

[1] Taylor to Evelyn, 16 April 1656, in John Evelyn, *Memoirs,* ed. William Bray (London, 1827), IV, 18.

[2] Ibid., IV, 21.

[3] John Evelyn, *Essay on . . . De Rerum Natura,* (London, 1656), preface, sig. A8v. Henceforth cited as *Essay.* In the preface Evelyn quoted Gassend's *De Vita et Moribus Epicuri* (1647).

[4] Evelyn, *Essay,* p. 108.   [5] Ibid., p. 133.

On the question of the void, however, Evelyn sided explicitly with Charleton and Gassend.

Touching which disseminated *Vacuum* and *Inane spaces* the most learned *Petrus Gassendus* maketh a famous illustration by depressing of wheat in a Bushel . . . I will not repeat the experiment because the curious have read it in his books and every man may see it exactly translated by Dr. Charleton.[1]

Where we say that Nature abhors a vacuum, Evelyn stated in Charleton's words, it is but in a 'metaphorical sense'.[2] A void is disseminated throughout nature. Like Charleton, Evelyn identified the vacuum with the *Thohu* or chaos of the book of *Genesis*.[3]

Finally, Evelyn enlisted atomism in the *defence* of religion. No mere chance, he argued, could fashion this complex and inter-related universe. For potent arguments in this vein, Evelyn cited Gassend and Charleton.

But if there be any who shall please to *dissent*, or desire a more evident demonstration of our former seeming *Paradox*, let the *Reader* consult the incomparable and often cited *Petrus Gassendus* his Animadversions on *Diog. Laert.* 1.10, p. 193 . . . or if he will be satisfied by tradition as it is rarely well explained to his hand in that learned digression of our ingenious *Dr. Charleton* where this our *Poets Theory* of Atomes is most artificially and perspiciously demonstrated.[4]

It is abundantly evident that Evelyn's starting point was the work of Charleton and Gassend. As was the case with so many others, Evelyn's interest in atomism may have first been awakened during his visit with the Newcastle group in the 1640s at Paris where, in all likelihood, he first learned of the work of the atomists.[5]

Evelyn's contribution to the acceptance of atomism was eagerly received by those close to him, and, of course, by those close to Hobbes and the others of the Newcastle Circle. Richard Brown, Evelyn's father-in-law, wrote an ode which was prefixed to the *Essay* in which he lauded the advent of the atomic doctrine.

> If Galilaeus with his new found glass,
> Former Invention doth so far surpass
> By bringing distant bodies to our sight
> And make it judge their shape by neerer light,
> How much have you oblig'd us? in whose mind
> Y' have coucht that cataract which made us blind,
> And given our Soul and optick can descrie
> Not things alone, but where their causes lie?[6]

---

[1] Evelyn, *Essay*, p. 135.　　　　[2] Ibid., p. 138.
[3] Ibid., p. 170.　　　　[4] Ibid., p. 172.
[5] Evelyn, *Memoirs*, II, 285.
[6] Richard Brown, 'On my Son Evelyn's Translation of the First Book of Lucretius', in Evelyn, *Essay*, p. 1.

Lucretius, Brown continued, held the key to nature's mysteries. As Galileo has unveiled the hitherto invisible stars, Lucretius has unmasked the hidden causes of phenomena.

> Lucretius English'd, Natures great Code
> And Digest too where has deep Law so show'd
> That what we thought mysteriously perplext
> Translated thus, both *comment* is and *text*.[1]

Finally, Brown exuberantly claimed, no one can now sensibly deny the existence of atoms and the void. 'And he that would no emptiness maintain/ Belyes himself, the Vacuum's in his Brain.'[2]

The famous poet and friend of Hobbes, Edmund Waller, also wrote a dedicatory poem to Evelyn. Waller's poem is interesting because he took a far more extreme Epicurean position than did Evelyn and Charleton. Waller loudly proclaimed the atheistic world-view of Lucretius, noting very specifically the political implications of it for the now king-less English Commonwealth.

> Lucretius with a stork-like fate
> Born and translated in a State
> Comes to proclaim in English verse
> No Monarch rules the Universe.
> But chance and *Atomes* make *this All*
> In order Democratical
> Without design, or Fate, or Force.[3]

This atheistic sentiment, of course, was rather embarrassing to Evelyn who added in the margin: 'Not that the Interpreter (Evelyn) doth justifie this irreligion of the Poet (Lucretius) whose arguments he afterwards refutes.'

In the decade following the return of the Newcastle Circle from the continent, Charleton, Evelyn and others did much to free atomism from its links with impiety. Their work was carried on in the years following by Robert Boyle and others, such as Joseph Glanvill and Ralph Cudworth. Boyle, however, played an even more important role in the integration of atomism into English science. Through his copious experimental 'natural histories' he worked to bring the mechanical philosophy, and therefore atomism, within the pale of the new experimental learning. In doing this, he performed an important service for Cartesianism and, especially, atomism.

[1] Richard Brown, 'Translation', in Evelyn, *Essay*, p. 1.
[2] Ibid., p. 2.
[3] Waller, poem dedicatory, in Evelyn, *Essay*, p. 3.

IX

ROBERT BOYLE'S
CORPUSCULARIANISM

ROBERT Boyle is a difficult figure to assess. Like many others of the seventeenth century, he is often portrayed by historians of science as far more 'modern' than is justifiable.[1] Doubtless, Boyle made important and lasting contributions to seventeenth-century science. Doubtless also, much of Boyle's celebrated experimentation was naïve and without fruitful method. It should, however, be emphasized that while Boyle's experiments so often came to nought, they nevertheless played an important role in the establishment of the mechanical philosophy and, with it, atomism in England.

In the 1650s, the atomic hypothesis was elaborated as part of 'physics'. Descartes, Hobbes, and Gassend, the great physicist-systematizers of the mid-seventeenth century, all realized that in dealing with the motions of invisible and undetectable particles they were going far beyond the bounds of certitude. For them, therefore, the study of physics consisted in delineating possible opinions, limited only by two considerations: these opinions were not to conflict with any experience, nor should they lead logically to any absurdity once the primary hypotheses were granted.[2]

All opinions which conformed to these requirements and to the tacit agreement to explain all phenomena by matter in motion were, according to the prevalent notion of physics, to be considered equal. Physics, after all, was not as certain as mathematics; there could be no apodictic proofs.

This intellectual democracy, which even admitted Margaret Cavendish's fancies,[3] went against the grain of many English natural philosophers. Some, like Newton, determined to find what certainty they could in the mathematical aspects of natural philosophy. Others, like the Baconians of the Royal Society, wished to ascertain the true mechanisms of God's nature through natural histories, i.e. through 'experience'. Robert Boyle, on the other hand, took still a third position. It was Boyle's purpose to 'prove'

---

[1] A notable exception is Louis T. More whose biography of Boyle, *The Life and Works of the Honourable Robert Boyle* (New York, 1944), and article 'Boyle as Alchemist', *J. Hist. Ideas* **2** (1941) 61–76, attempt to give a more balanced picture of him.

[2] See for example Hobbes, in Hist. MSS Comm., *Portland Manuscripts* (London, 1891), II, p. 128, and Descartes, *Oeuvres*, III, 178–9.

[3] See Duke of Newcastle's comments quoted in A. S. Turberville, *History of Welbeck Abbey and Its Owners* (London, 1938), I, 185.

the truth of the mechanical philosophy and determine the validity of the philosophers' mechanisms, when possible, through experimental investigations.[1]

In this endeavour Boyle was, in a sense, in the tradition of Bacon. Boyle was, as it were, a Baconian let loose upon the theoretical structures of Descartes and Gassend. To be sure, Descartes, Gassend, and Charleton explicated their systems through illustrative experiments. Boyle, however, went far beyond these earlier efforts both in number of experiments and in technique. Boyle filled a gap which many Englishmen after Bacon had keenly felt: the atomist and Cartesian structures were admittedly admirable, rational systems, but did they conform to experience?

Armed with the new laboratory techniques developed in the seventeenth century, Boyle was able to search for the same certainty upon which Bacon had insisted in the *New Organon*. The search was doomed to failure; experimental and theoretical techniques which could permit success were not to be developed for over 200 years. Still, his efforts to substantiate the mechanical philosophies of Descartes and Gassend, both of which he grouped under the generic name 'corpuscular philosophy', did succeed in impressing his contemporaries. To his fellow members of the Royal Society he was the champion of the mechanical philosophy—the one scientist who exhaustively illustrated it by experiment.[2]

With respect to the corpuscular philosophy itself, Boyle was not an original theorist. He added little, if anything, to the theories of Descartes or Gassend. It has been claimed, without firm foundation, that Boyle's corpuscularianism was 'an independent development along lines suggested by Bacon'.[3] On the contrary, Boyle's contributions were experimental rather than theoretical; he was, *as he himself often stated*, merely attempting to bring the existing corpuscular philosophies within the pale of the new experimental learning:

I hoped [Boyle wrote] I might at least do no unseasonable piece of service to the corpuscular philosophies by illustrating some of their notions with sensible experiments.[4]

The above quotation is the key to Boyle's experimental endeavours. He was indeed trying to illustrate the corpuscular philosophy by experient. But it must again be stressed that he himself possessed no great power as a theorist. He retained, in fact, a scepticism toward all theories; he was a 'good Baconian' in the sense in which the term came to be defined in

[1] Robert Boyle, *Works of the Honorable Robert Boyle,* ed. T. Birch (London, 1772), I, 356. Henceforth cited as *Works.*
[2] Henry Oldenburg, Epistle dedicatory to Boyle, *Phil. Trans. R. Soc.* 5 (1670) 1143–6.
[3] Marie Boas, 'Establishment of the Mechanical Philosophy', *Osiris* 10 (1952) 461.
[4] Boyle, *Works,* I, 356.

practice throughout the early history of the Royal Society. Boyle looked to the corpuscular philosophy primarily as an heuristic instrument to lead to new experiments and observations.

Such writings of very learned men [he maintained] although they may bear very general titles, yet are not published by their authors as compleat bodies or system of physiology, *but rather as general principles* . . . to assist men to explicate the already known phenomena of nature. For of such writings if their authors be (as for the most part they are) subtile and inquisitive men, there may be good use . . . because their writers, to make good their new opinions must either bring new experiments and observations or else must consider those that are already known after a new manner, and thereby make us take notice of something unheeded before.[1]

When Boyle did express his views on the nature of matter, they were close to those of Gassend and Descartes. Indeed, as Boyle often stated, he did not wish, or was not able experimentally, to distinguish between the two. Thus, he very often refused to take a stand between them where they differed, and merely juxtaposed atomist and Cartesian explanations. The prefaces to many of his experimental studies attest to this neutrality and purpose.[2]

The young Boyle had ample opportunity to become acquainted with the works of the French corpuscularians, not only through published works, but through his own friends. Boyle was, for example, associated with several of the members of the Newcastle Circle; he was associated with John Pell,[3] and corresponded with his 'affectionate friend' and anatomy tutor, William Petty.[4] He also corresponded with John Evelyn,[5] and in the 1650s made frequent expressions of admiration for his kinsman, Kenelm Digby.[6] Very early Boyle learned of Gassend's synthesis of Epicurean philosophy from another friend and correspondent, Samuel Hartlib. In May 1648, Hartlib wrote:

Your worthy friend and mine, Mr. Gassend is reasonable well. . . . He hath now in press at *Lyons* the *Philosophy of Epicurus* in which I believe we shall have much of his own philosophy, which doubtless will be an excellent work.[7]

All the early influences upon Boyle—Gassend, Descartes, Digby, and others—appear in an early manuscript probably written about 1650, entitled 'Of the Atomicall Philosophy'.[8] Below the title appears an

[1] Boyle, *Works,* I, 301–02.   [2] Ibid., IV, 236; III, 7; I, 310.
[3] Ibid., I, lviii.   [4] Ibid., VI, 137.
[5] Ibid., I, lvii.   [6] M. Boas, *Boyle,* p. 25.
[7] Boyle, *Works,* VI, 77. The work of which Hartlib wrote was the *Animadversiones* of 1649. The general title *Philosophy of Epicurus* (*Epicuri Philosophia*) appears on the leaf before the title page.
[8] The manuscript was first published by Richard Westfall, 'Unpublished Boyle Papers Relating to Scientific Method', part II, *Ann. Sci.* **12** (1956) 111–13. The title was crossed out by Boyle.

admonishment which reflects Boyle's hesitancy to link himself publicly
with a philosophy so tainted with atheism: 'These Papers are without fayle
to be burn't.'[1]

Despite this sombre message, the manuscript itself is an innocuous
exhortation to natural philosophers to consider more seriously the 'Atomicall Philosophy invented or brought into request by Democritus, Leucippus, and their Contemporaries'. After centuries of unfortunate suppression,
Boyle wrote, 'in our lesse partial & more inquisitive times it is so luckly
reviv'd & so skillfully celebrated in divers parts of Europe by the learned
pens of Gassendus, Magnenus, Des Cartes & his disciples our deservedly
famous Sr Kenelme Digby & many other writers.'[2]

According to Boyle, the views of Democritus and Epicurus have been
misrepresented; these men only maintained the existence of naturally
indivisible particles, but not of indivisible points.[3] The existence of atoms
in nature, as the modern atomists view them, is highly probable. '[T]hat
there are Atomes in the notion freshly given of them seems very
probably [*sic*] not only because as we just now observ'd nature not being
able in her resolutions endlessly to sub-divide by the last subdivisions shee
can make, must necessarily constitute Atomes, but because most of
the Phenomena of Nature doe seeme to evince the being of Atomes
by seeming to be productions of Atomes so and so qualified and
dispos'd.'[4]

Boyle's early adherence to atomism, properly so called, was soon qualified in another work written in the early 1650s entitled *Some Considerations
Touching the Usefulness of Experimental Natural Philosophy* and which appeared
in the early 1660s. This work is a graphic illustration of the influence of
Bacon upon Boyle and of the latter's interest in physical theology. In it,
man is depicted as the 'minister of nature'.[5] Natural philosophy, Boyle also
maintained, is useful also as a proof of the existence of God.[6] The *Considerations* are primarily interesting in this regard: in it, Boyle first gave thought
to vexing problems associated with religious implications of atomism, and
quickly dissociated himself from Epicurean world-makers, 'those modern
admirers of Epicurus', who banish God from the universe by declaring the
possibility of universal creation by the casual dance of atoms.[7] To which
'modern admirers of Epicurus' was Boyle referring? He certainly did not
mean Gassend or Charleton who readily denied the atheistic atomism of the
pagans. More probably Boyle was referring to Hobbes or Lady Margaret
of Newcastle, for the latter claimed publicly that 'small Atoms of them-

[1] Ibid., p. 111.   [2] Ibid., p. 111.
[3] Westfall, 'Unpublished Boyle Papers', pp. 111–12.   [4] Ibid., pp. 112–13.
[5] Boyle, *Works,* II, 14.   [6] Ibid. II, 19–20.
[7] Boyle, *Works,* II, 40–43.

selves a World may make'.[1] Boyle was particularly chagrined to meet those, like Hobbes and Lady Margaret, who denied the existence of immortal and incorporeal spirits. 'I meet with some', Boyle wrote, 'as the Epicureans, who tell me they cannot frame a notion of an incorporeal substance nor spirit'.[2]

The atomism of Gassend and Charleton was, however, free from these objections, and by the late 1650s Boyle was openly adopting both Epicurean and Cartesian theories. An advertisement to *Certain Physiological Essays* (1661) which were written *c.* 1659 claimed that Boyle wrote to please those 'addicted to the Epicurean philosophy; the author's explicating things chiefly according to the atomical principles will not be . . . looked upon as a sure argument of his being wedded to the particular opinions wherein the atomists differ from other Naturalists'.[3] The theories expounded in the *History of Fluidity* and the *History of Firmness* were identical with those of the Epicurean atomist Charleton, except for Boyle's typical obeisances to the Cartesian viewpoint.

In 1654 Charleton had written:	Boyle wrote, *c.* 1659:
Fluidity we conceive to be a quality arising meerly from hence;	A body then seems to be fluid, chiefly upon this account
that the Atoms or insensible particles of which a fluid concretion doth consist are smooth in superfice and reciprocally contiguous in others	that it consists of corpuscles that touching one another in some parts only of their surface (and so being incontiguous in the rest)
so that many inane spaces . . . being interspersed among them	
they are upon the motion of the mass or body which they compose, most easily moveable, rowling one upon another, and in a continued fluor or stream diffusing themselves	and separately agitated to and fro, can by reason of the numerous pores or spaces necessarily left betwixt their contiguous parts easily glide along each other's superficies, and by reason of their motion diffuse themselves
till they are arrested by some firm body to whose superfice they exactly accommodate themselves.[4]	till they meet with some hard or resting body; to whose internal surface . . . they exquisitely, as to sense, accommodate themselves.[5]

[1] Margaret Cavendish, *Poems,* p. 5.
[2] Boyle, *Works,* II, 47.
[3] Boyle, *Works,* I, 377.
[4] Charleton, *Physiologia,* p. 318.
[5] Ibid., I, 378.

It is difficult to tell whether Boyle has here paraphrased Charleton's *Physiologia* or Gassend's *Animadversiones*.[1] Gassend's version has 'interior surface' in the last paragraph as does Boyle; Charleton omitted this superfluous word. Boyle has also, out of deference to the Cartesians omitted any reference to 'void spaces' and the term 'atom' has been replaced by 'corpuscle'.

A comparison of Boyle's *History of Firmness* with the *Physiologia* of Charleton and the *Animadversiones* of Gassend seems to show that Boyle relied upon Charleton's version.

Charleton (1654) had written:

Boyle (*c.* 1659) wrote:

And as for the other General Quality, Firmness or Stability, Since contraries must have Contrary Causes, and that the solidity of Atoms is the fundament of all solidity and firmness in Concretions

And since fluidness and stability being contrary Qualities are to be apprehended under contrary notions

well may we understand it to be radicated in this

we may conceive that the firmness or stability of a body consists principally in this

that the insensible particles of which a Firme Concretion is composed (whether they be of one or diverse worts, i.e. similar or dissimilar in magnitude and figure)

that the particles that compose it besides that they are most commonly gross

do so reciprocally compress and adhaere unto each other as that being uncapable of rowling upon each other superfice, both in respect of the ineptitude of their figures thereunto, and the want of competent inane spaces among them

either do so rest or are so intangled between themselves that there is among them a mutual cohesion

they generally become incapable (without extream violence) of Emotion, Dissociation, Diffusion

whereby they are rendered unapt to flow or diffuse themselves every way and consequently to be, without violence,

and so of termination by any other superfice but what they themselves constitute.[2]

bounded and figured by other surfaces than those which their connection makes themselves constitute.[3]

---

[1] Gassend, *Animadversiones in decimum librum Diogenis Laertii* (Lyons, 1649), I, 333.
[2] Charleton, *Physiologia*, p. 320.   [3] Boyle, *Works*, I, 401.

The passages of both Boyle and Charleton are similar to the *Animadversiones* of Gassend.[1] Boyle in his treatment of firmness or stability has done again what he was to do often in later years: he has juxtaposed Cartesian ('either do so rest') and Epicurean ('or are intangeled between themselves') explanations, and has avoided points of conflict between the two systems.

Where in all this is Boyle's 'own theory'? Here, in his early work, as in his later treatises concerning the mechanical philosophy, Boyle has merely offered, side by side, Cartesian and atomist explanations. If this be an original or distinct theory, it has yet to be shown. Marie Boas has attempted to prove Boyle's originality without evident success.[2] In part, her attempt is based upon her view of the theories of Gassend and Bacon: she tries to depict Bacon as an atomist and a mechanist[3] perhaps overlooking the pitfalls of this representation;[4] Gassend's atomism is dismissed as 'static',[5] a misconception which leads Miss Boas to ignore totally Gassend's *Animadversiones*.

Miss Boas has maintained (correctly) that Boyle's *Origins of Forms and Qualities according to the Corpuscular Philosophy* (1666) is a 'really complete exposition of Boyle's own views on the underlying structure of matter, and also an enunciation of the "corpuscular philosophy" Boyle's own version of the mechanical philosophy', for '[n]ever again did Boyle discuss his theory of matter in such detail.'[6] The *Origins of Forms and Qualities* must, therefore, serve as a test case for Boyle's originality as theorist of the corpuscular philosophy.

In this work, as in most but not all others, Boyle refused to judge between the Cartesian or Epicurean atomist views.

I have forborn [he wrote] to imploy arguments that are either grounded on, or suppose indivisible corpuscles called Atoms, or any innate motion belonging to them; or that the essence of bodies consists in extension, or that a vacuum is impossible; or that there are such *globuli coelestes* or such a *materia subtilis* as the *Cartesians* imploy to explicate most of the phaenomena of nature. For these and divers other notions I (who here write rather for the Corpuscularians in general, than any part of them) thought it needlessly to take in discoursing . . . against those to whom these things appear as disputable.[7]

---

[1] Gassend, *Animadversiones*, I, 338–42.

[2] See her 'Establishment of the Mechanical Philosophy', (above, p. 94, note 3), *Robert Boyle and the Seventeenth-Century Chemistry* (p. 95, note 6), and 'Boyle as a Theoretical Scientist', *Isis* 41 (1950) 261–8.

[3] Marie Boas, 'Hero's Pneumatica, a Study of Its Transmission and Influence', *Isis* 40 (1949) 48.

[4] See above, Chapter V.

[5] Boas, *Boyle*, p. 80.

[6] Boas, 'Establishment', pp. 467–9.

[7] Boyle, *Works*, III, 7.

The 'corpuscular philosophy' of which he wrote in the *Origins of Forms and Qualities* was therefore a generalization of the theories of the two competing corpuscularian sects, i.e. a presentation of those opinions upon which they agreed. In no very useful sense was this an original theory, nor was it the 'culmination' of the mechanical philosophy.[1]

Boyle's corpuscular philosophy can briefly be summarized in the following fashion. Matter exists as a *prima materia*, 'extended, divisible and impenetrable', endowed with motion by God.[2] Matter and motion are at the root of all physical phenomena. The *prima materia* exists in the form of particles or corpuscles which are divisible mentally or by God but nature does 'scarce ever actually divide' them.[3] The particles form concretions which are actually the primary building blocks of nature. Differences in the size, shape, and motion of these constituent concretions account for the differences in colour, odour, taste, etc. of bodies which are found in the visible world.[4]

The above summary, it should be noted, could also serve to describe the Epicurean atomist and Cartesian position. Much has been made of the role of *motion* in 'Boyle's theory'.[5] However, no one has shown how Boyle's use of motion was significantly different from those of the other corpuscularians. If, to be sure, Boyle's use of motion was different in an important way, a clarification of this point would be most welcome. Until this clarification is forthcoming, Boyle's service to the mechanical philosophy must be restricted to the effect of the experiments which he hoped would illuminate existing theories.

Boyle's experimental work dealing with the mechanical philosophy all attest to the attitude which we have described: namely, Boyle's reluctance to choose between atomist and Cartesian explanations. In his *Experimental History of Colours* (1664) he quoted Gassend with admiration, yet once again Boyle refused to commit himself to a preference between Descartes and the atomists.

[T]hough this be at present the hypothesis I prefer, yet I propose it but in a general sense, teaching only that the beams of light modified by the bodies whence they are sent . . . to the eye produce there that kind of sensation men commonly call colour.[6]

Another example of Boyle's reluctance can be found in the essay *Of the Mechanical Origins of Heat and Cold* (1675). While inclining to the view (held

[1] Boas, 'Hero's Pneumatica', p. 48.
[2] Boyle, *Works*, III, 15. Miss Boas gives an accurate summary in 'Establishment', pp. 467–9.
[3] Boyle, *Works*, III, 29.   [4] Ibid., III, 31–35.
[5] Boas, 'Establishment', p. 469.   [6] Boyle, *Works*, I, 695.

by the Cartesians) that cold is a privation of the motion which constitutes heat, Boyle still wished in some way to include the Epicurean notion that cold is a positive quality. Gassend attributed cold to the slowing and deadening action of *frigorifick* particles. Boyle wrote:

For if it be true (as we there shew) the nature of heat consists either only or chiefly in the local motion of small parts of a body ... and if it be also true, as experience witnesses it to be, that when the minute parts of a body are ... more slowly or faintly agitated than those of our fingers ... we judge them cold: these two things ... seem plainly enough to argue that a privation or negation of that local motion ... may suffice for the demonstrating a body cold.[1]

This theory of cold is certainly a kinetic one, but Boyle proceeded to include the Epicurean position:

And though its effect, which is coldness, seem a privation or negation, yet the cause of it may be a positive agent acting mechanically, by clogging the agile calorifick particles, or deadening their motion, or perverting their determination, or by some other intelligible way bringing them to a state of coldness as to sense.[2]

Hence, even on the question of heat and cold, Boyle wished to placate all parties among the mechanical philosophers.

When dealing with the corpuscular philosophy, Boyle's experimental goal was to illustrate and illuminate the theories of the atomists and Cartesians. His later works dealing with the mechanical philosophy all demonstrate quite clearly his attempt to illustrate the works of the corpuscularians. His *Essays of the Strange Subtilty, Great Efficacy and Determinate Nature of Effluviums* (1673) was undertaken to show merely that, experimentally, the nature of effluvia was not inconsistent with contemporary theories.

[M]y present purpose [he wrote] ... is only to shew that the wonderful minuteness I shall hereafter ascribe to effluvia is not inconsistent with the most received theories of naturalists.[3]

The most ambitious attempt to bring the theories of the corpuscular philosophers within the Baconian experimental tradition was Boyle's *Experiments, Notes, etc. about the Mechanical Origins or Production of Divers Particular Qualities* (1675). Once again Boyle wished, not to act as arbiter between the atomists and Cartesians, but to demonstrate the efficacy of both approaches as opposed to the scholastic or the 'chemical' doctrines.

[M]y purpose in these notes [Boyle stated] was rather to shew, it was not necessary to betake ourselves to the scholastick or chemical doctrine about qualities, then to act the umpire between the differing hypotheses of the Corpuscularians.[4]

[1] Boyle, *Works,* IV, 244.
[3] Ibid., III, 661.
[2] Ibid., IV, 244.
[4] Ibid., IV, 236

Since a great deal has been written about the experimental basis for Boyle's corpuscularianism,[1] it perhaps would be useful to examine the *Experiments, Notes, etc. about the Mechanical Origins . . . of Qualities* in some detail. Boyle, in these essays, aimed merely at rendering the mechanical philosophy plausible in the minds of his readers; he made no pretence of certain proof. '[T]hat, which I need to prove', he wrote, 'is, not that mechanical principles are the necessary and only things, whereby qualities may be explained, but that probably they will be found sufficient for their explication'.[2] In estimating Boyle's success, the modern reader will constantly have to remind himself that Boyle was contending against Aristotelians for seventeenth century minds. In modern terms, Boyle's attempt is often ludicrous in its failure; his contemporaries, however, found him convincing. The reason is simple: Boyle rarely addressed himself directly to the problem of experimentally testing the mechanical philosophy, or even to the task of making the mechanical origins of particular qualities plausible. What he often did do, and convincingly to his contemporaries, was to undercut the arguments of his opponents.

In the essay, *Of the Mechanical Origin of Heat and Cold,* for example, Boyle's ten experiments relating to the production of cold deal primarily with the mixing of chemicals.[3] In the first experiment, he took sal ammoniac and mixed it with water and found that the mixture becomes very cold. In the second trial, he repeated the first experiment, but this time with warmed ingredients. Similarly, the resultant mixture turned very cold. These two experiments demonstrated, at least to Boyle, 'that . . . a far more intense degree of cold may emerge in this mixture, than was to be found in either of the ingredients before they were mingled'.[4] This seemed to indicate to Boyle that the coldness produced 'probably referred to some change of texture resulting from the action of the liquor upon the salt'.[5] The latter proposal was more supposition than inference, but the major goal was accomplished: to embarrass the Aristotelians by stripping away their forms and qualities. How, Boyle asked, could cold emerge from two chemicals, especially from two to which heat had been added?

Experiment VI of the same series is particularly characteristic. It was known that saltpetre placed in water produced cold. The *cold* was not a quality of the saltpetre, Boyle showed, by producing *heat* using the same salt placed in liquid other than water, in this case, oil of vitriol. The two, when mixed, produced considerable heat.

---

[1] Cf. Marie Boas, 'Establishment', pp. 461–2.
[2] Boyle, *Works,* IV, 232.   [3] Ibid., pp. 236–42.
[4] Ibid., IV, 237.   [5] Ibid.

In experiment I, Boyle had placed sal ammoniac in water and produced cold. Elsewhere, he mixed oil of vitriol and sal ammoniac and also produced cold. In experiment VIII, he mixed all three and produced not *cold,* but *heat.* He performed this experiment 'to shew further, what influence motion and texture may have upon such trials'.[1] It is easy to see that he did no such thing, but rather attempted to show that the production of heat or cold was independent of any supposed innate form or quality of heat or cold. In short, Boyle's experiments showed little or nothing about the plausibility of the mechanical philosophy (his stated goal), but rather damaged the opposing theory (the Aristotelian framework). The mechanical philosophy was expected to rush into the resulting breach. Corpuscularianism was to win by default.

Boyle's experiments on the mechanical production of tastes are equally instructive. Boyle took two bodies of bland taste, mixed them and found the resultant mixture to be corrosive or fiery. Secondly he took an insipid chemical (e.g. saltpetre) and by distillation rendered it corrosive. Thirdly, he took a salty body and a sweet body and created a bland or insipid mixture. These trials, he claimed, he could best explain mechanically. For example, Boyle accounted for the breaking down of normally bland saltpetre into a corrosive or sharp chemical by fire in the following fashion:

I have sometimes considered, whether the phaenomena of these two experiments may not be explicated, by supposing them to arise from the new magnitudes and figures of the particles, which the fire, by breaking them, or forcibly rubbing them one against the other, or also against the corpuscles of the additament, may be presumed to give them; as if, for example, since we find the larger and best formed crystals of nitre to be of a prismatical shape with six sides, we should suppose the corpuscles of nitre to be little prisms, whose angles and ends are too obtuse or blunt to make vigorous and deep impressions on the tongue; and yet, if these little prisms be by a violent heat split . . . they may come to have parts so much smaller than before, and endowed with such sharp sides, and angles, that, being dissolved . . . their smallness may give them great access to the pores [of the tongue] and the sharpness of their sides and points may fit them to stab and cut . . .[2]

In the section on the mechanical production of odours, Boyle continued to undercut the Aristotelian framework without truly making the corpuscularian explanation plausible. He produced odours different from those of the mixed bodies; he produced an odour in a non-odourous body merely by adding water; he took two malodourous bodies and produced a fragrant mixture. Could these be explained by Aristotelian forms and qualities? Boyle thought not, and his fellow virtuosi agreed with him.[3]

[1] Boyle, *Works,* IV, 242.
[2] Ibid., IV, 259.
[3] Ibid., pp. 267–73.
8

In relatively few experiments, therefore, did Boyle directly attack the problem of the relationship of the mechanical philosophy and the production of qualities. These experiments did, however, exist. In discussing the production of heat, for example, Boyle pointed to the heating of a nail by hammering. Merely by adding or impressing a mechanical movement onto the metal, heat is generated.

When for example, a smith does hastily hammer a nail, or such like piece of iron, the hammered metal will grow exceedingly hot, and yet there appears not anything to make it so, save the forcible motion of the hammer, which impresses a vehement, and variously determined agitation of the small parts of the iron.[1]

Similarly, Boyle recounted the mechanical production of odours, via heat, or by friction as wood being turned on a lathe.[2] But these direct confrontations are relatively less numerous (and less successful) than Boyle's attempts at destroying the opposing view.

In sum, it was the experimental 'verification' or the weight of positive experimental evidence which Boyle brought to bear which convinced his contemporaries of the truth of corpuscularianism. His audience was an eager one, all too willing to gather further 'evidence' of the demise of Aristotelianism, and to accept the 'purified' mechanical philosophy.

As Boyle himself maintained, with respect to theory he was partial to the views of 'the antient corpuscular philosophers (whose doctrine in most other points but not in all we are most inclinable to)'.[3] In his religious fastidiousness, Boyle could not of course accept the ancient atomism without qualification. Like other pious corpuscularians such as Gassend and Charleton, Boyle insisted upon God's authorship of the world and His providence in maintaining it.[4] He also insisted that motion is not inherent in matter, a particularly abhorrent doctrine of antiquity. The doctrine of uncreated time and space was likewise unacceptable to Boyle. As Gassend viewed them, time and space differ from the rest of nature; they are uncreated, antecedent to creation, and would survive the universe should God choose to annihilate it. Such limitations upon God were unacceptable to Boyle.[5]

In England Boyle's efforts to establish the mechanical philosophy met with scarcely qualified success. A list of testimonials to the impact which

---

[1] Boyle, *Works,* IV, 249.   [2] Ibid., p. 268.
[3] Ibid., III, 15.   [4] Ibid., II, 39.
[5] Ibid., VI, 684. See also Harold Fisch, 'Scientist as Priest', *Isis* **44** (1953) 254; Richard Hunt, *The Place of Religion in the Science of Robert Boyle* (Pittsburgh, 1955), *passim*; Robert A. Greene, 'Henry More and Robert Boyle on the Spirit of Nature', *J. Hist. Ideas* **23** (1962) 451–74; Wilbur Applebaum, 'Boyle and Hobbes: a Reconsideration', *J. Hist. Ideas* **25** (1964) 117–19.

Boyle made upon famous commentators such as Glanvill, Dryden, Wotton, Bentley, MacLaurin, *et al.,* would be tedious. Let it suffice to say that most of Boyle's countrymen were satisfied that he had 'restored' the corpuscular philosophy by his ingenious experimentation.[1]

There are two reasons why Boyle's influence was crucial to the acceptance of corpuscularianism (and with it, atomism) in England, over and above any theological implications. His experimental approach to the mechanical philosophy went beyond any similar attempts of his contemporaries in comprehensiveness and sheer bulk. Secondly, and perhaps even more significantly, Boyle published his work during a period in which there was a fertile field for the reception of such an anti-Aristotelian, mechanical philosophy, grounded hopefully in the experimental tradition of Bacon. The Royal Society, of which Boyle was an original member, provided a willing and interested public for the essays which he published in the 1660s and later. Through the combination of appropriate method and content, and fortunate timing, Boyle played an unquestionably important role in the establishment of atomism in England in the seventeenth century.

[1] Boas, 'Establishment', p. 484.

X

THE ROYAL SOCIETY, EXPERIMENTAL PHILOSOPHY, AND THE HYPOTHETICAL PHYSICS

'Hypothesis: A sort of System laid down from ones own Imagination . . . to account for some *Phaenomenon* or appearance in Nature.'

JOHN HARRIS, *Lexicon Technicum* (5th Ed., 1736)

THE Royal Society was, at its founding in 1662, Baconian in spirit, temper, and practice. Most scholars of the period are in agreement with this assessment. Yet, what precisely did the term 'Baconian' connote during the early Restoration? Certainly, all self-proclaimed Baconians revered 'experiment' and deplored 'fancy'. It must be remembered, however, that both terms were employed in a variety of ways, and it will become important to sort them out. The important link between all Baconians, it will be found, is their common goal of certainty through experience.

Bacon, it will be recalled, proposed to establish successive stages of certainty in science through his new organon.[1] He criticized severely those natural philosophers 'who have taken upon them to lay down the law of nature as a thing already searched out and understood', for these philosophers, 'whether they have spoken in simple assurances or professional affectation, have done philosophy and the sciences a great injury'.[2] The new organon, or method, on the other hand makes no such claims. It would establish certainty by relying on the evidence of the senses, corrected and aided by safeguards, but rejecting 'the mental operation which follows the act of sense'.[3] Instead of that operation, Bacon would 'open and lay out a new and certain path for the mind to proceed in'.[4] He advocated a path to understanding, 'direct from the sense, by a course of experiment orderly conducted and well built up'.[5] Bacon was, however, aware of the danger of blind empiricism.

But the true method of experience [Bacon wrote in the *Novum Organum*] on the contrary, first lights the candle, and then by means of the candle shows the way;

[1] Bacon, *Works,* VIII, 60.　　　　　[2] Ibid., VIII, 59.
[3] Ibid., VIII, 60.　　　　　　　　　　[4] Ibid.
[5] Ibid., VIII, 114.

commencing as it does with experience duly ordered and digested, not bungling or erratic, and from it educing exioms . . .[1]

It was from such considerations of method that Bacon was forced to abandon Greek atomism. The Baconians of the Royal Society digested these methodological precepts, and (although inconsistently) attempted to put them into practice. An extremely important point to focus attention upon is that Bacon's call for 'certainty' was at variance with the type of physics prevalent in the 1650s. Descartes, Hobbes, and Gassend, who dominated physics at that time, were therefore subjected to the Royal Society's scrutiny in the light of a well advanced, 'Baconian' scepticism of theory.

The three great mechanical philosophers—Descartes, Gassend, and Hobbes—were all aware of a deep contradiction in the mechanical philosophy. The mechanical world-view purported to explain all natural phenomena by the size, shape, and motion of invisible particles of matter. Yet these particles or corpuscles were not amenable to direct experience, nor could their motions be educed with any sort of mathematical rigour. Physics was, in consequence, necessarily *hypothetical*. Unlike mathematics, physics was not, and could never be, rigorous, precisely because the particles which are the source of physical qualities could never be treated in a rigorous fashion. It was the role of the physicist, therefore, to suggest 'hypotheses' or detailed mechanisms which were *possible* or *plausible*. He could do little else. These detailed mechanisms, or hypotheses, were limited only by three conditions. First, they had to be consistent with observed phenomena; secondly, they had to be consistent with the basic premises of the system; thirdly, they had to be self-consistent and lead to no absurdity.

All three mechanical philosophers were, therefore, also 'hypothetical physicists'. For example, as early as 1636 Hobbes wrote:

In thinges that are not demonstrable, of which kind is the greatest part of naturall philosophy, as depending upon the motion of bodies so subtile as they are invisible, such as are ayre and spirits, the most that can be atteyned unto is to have such opinions, as no certayne experience can confute, and from which can be deduced by lawfull argumentation no absurdity.[2]

Hobbes proposed such hypotheses in his *De Corpore*; they were suggested only tentatively, as he maintained all explanations in physics must be.[3] Similarly, in his essay, *Seven Philosophical Problems*, first published in 1662, Hobbes wrote: 'The Doctrine of Naturall Causes hath not infallible and

[1] Bacon, *Works,* VIII, 115.
[2] T. Hobbes to Newcastle, July 1636, in Historical Manuscripts Commission, *Portland Manuscripts* (London, 1891), II, 128.
[3] Hobbes, *Works,* I, 531.

evident Principles. For there is noe Effect which the power of God cannot produce by many severall wayes.'[1]

Hobbes' words, and sentiments, were strikingly similar to those of Descartes. In the *Principia Philosophiae*, Descartes asserted that, regarding the invisible motions which are at the root of physical qualities, the natural philosopher can only demonstrate *how things could possibly be*; to illuminate the possible and probable hidden mechanisms is the purpose of corpuscular physics.

It is certain [Descartes wrote] that God has an infinity of diverse methods by which he could have made all the things of this world appear as they now appear, and it is impossible for the human spirit to know which of all these methods he wished to employ.[2]

Thus, Descartes concluded, it is the function of the physicist to suggest possible and internally consistent hypotheses; he can accomplish little else. A fuller statement of Descartes' position can be found in a letter to Mersenne in 1638. In it, Descartes insisted that

To require of me geometrical demonstrations in a question which concerns physics is to ask me to do the impossible . . . [In such matters we have to rely on suppositions] which, even if they are not exactly true, are yet not manifestly contrary to experience, and in speaking of which we argue consistently, without falling into paralogisms . . . Take it therefore, that there are only two ways of refuting what I have written, either that of proving by certain experiences or reasons that the things I have supposed are false, or else of showing that what I have deduced from them cannot be so deduced.[3]

For Gassend, the empiricist, as for Descartes the rationalist, natural philosophy was constrained to remain conjectural and hypothetical.[4] Gassend developed what has been called a 'constructive scepticism' in his efforts to establish atomism as a viable mechanical philosophy.[5] Because there is lacking an experiential basis for our examinations of the sub-visible world of atoms and void, he claimed, we can never attain the certainty for which Bacon strove. Perhaps Gassend would have seen clearly the futility of the seventeenth-century Baconian corpuscularians: one could establish according to Bacon's canons neither atomism nor Cartesianism. Certainly, Bacon saw the similar problem in his abandonment of the atomic philosophy. Thus, Gassend's empiricism and his elaborate and detailed atomic mechanisms can be reconciled in his 'hypothetical physics'.[6]

[1] B.M. Harley MSS. 3360, f. 1.

[2] Descartes, *Oeuvres*, III, 520–1.

[3] Descartes to Mersenne, 27 May 1638, quoted in Norman Kemp Smith, *New Studies in the Philosophy of Descartes* (London, 1952), pp. 96–7.

[4] Pierre Gassend, *Opera Omnia*, III, 192.

[5] Richard Popkin, *The History of Scepticism from Erasmus to Descartes* (Assen, 1960), p. 106.

[6] See also Bernard Rochot, 'La vraie philosophie de Gassendi' in *Actes du congrès du tricentaire de Pierre Gassendi* (Digne, 1957), pp. 227–47.

In the 1660s, there was, in England, a reaction against this 'hypothetical physics' to which the mechanical philosophers were chained. This reaction occurred on a broad front; it was not confined to a few isolated natural philosophers. Indeed, the Royal Society was, in part, the institutionalized protest of this turn from the systematizers, despite the enormous influence of the mechanical philosophers upon it. Bacon was the prophet; Boyle, Glanvill, and the others were his willing disciples.

Bacon's call for *certainty* in science was echoed by his followers. Yet, the revolt against the hypothetical physics took several forms; there was a spectrum of Baconians opposed to the excesses of the hypothesizers (although not necessarily to their mechanical principles). First, there were those in the Royal Society who rejected *all* theories, and fell back upon elaborate 'natural histories' after the fashion of some of Bacon's treatises. These 'empirics' claimed it was too early to utilize or pretend to theory; collections of facts were all that, at present, could be attained. Secondly, there were those, like Robert Boyle, who (despite concessions to the empirics) attempted to *test* the great systems of Descartes and Gassend. Boyle was not satisfied with the *a priori* nature of the systems of the French philosophers, and wished, through experimental investigations such as the *Experiments, Notes, etc. about the Mechanical Origins . . . of Qualities,* to investigate the manner of their conformity with experience.[1] Finally, there were those like Isaac Barrow and Isaac Newton, who accepted Bacon's demand for certainty, and, not finding it in the hypothetical physics, emphasized the necessity for what they called 'mathematics' and what today would be called 'mathematical physics'.[2]

It was during the early years after the establishment of the Royal Society that the 'vulgar Baconian' or 'empiric' reaction against the hypothetical physics began to be clearly evident, and the word 'hypothesis' often began to be used as a pejorative. The Puritan divine, Richard Baxter, for example, wrote in *The Reasons of the Christian Religion*:

And by what proof do you distinguish matter into those degrees, or sorts, any more than into two, or four, or six or ten, or ten hundred? Who can choose but shake the head, to see wise Philosophers thus impose upon the world, and at the same time say, It is the first duty of a man that would be wise to believe no more than by evidence he is forced to? Yea, and at the same time to say, *These are but our Hypotheses, which saith one I acknowledge to be false, and saith another, I cannot say is true: and yet, they are our foundations*; and from these our philosophical Verities result; which must make you wise, who must believe nothing without proof. Alas, what is man![3]

[1] See above, Chapter IX.
[2] See above, Chapter XI.
[3] Richard Baxter, *The Reasons of the Christian Religion* (London, 1667), p. 509. Henceforth cited as *Reasons*. Emphasis supplied.

Baxter was, of course, using the arguments of the mechanical philosophers against them; he was referring particularly to the systems of Descartes, Hobbes, and Gassend, although the last he exonerated of any excesses against the immateriality of the soul, one of Baxter's chief concerns.[1]

How, Baxter asked, can true philosophy rest upon hypotheses admitted by their authors to be (at least) without certainty? And without this certainty, he continued, what right have the mechanical philosophers to undermine received philosophy and true religion? The spread of the mechanical philosophy was aiding impiety, and was itself aided by narrowness and ignorance.

I find also, [Baxter wrote] that the most who in this age adhere to the *Epicurean* (or *Cartesian*) Hypothesis are the younger sort of ingenious men, who have received prejudice against the *Peripateticks*, *Platonists* and *Stoicks* before they did ever thoroughly study them . . . [The Epicureans] look so much at things corporeal, that they quite over-look the noblest natures, and they reduce all to *Matter* and *Motion* because nothing but *Matter* and *Motion* is thoroughly studied by them.[2]

While Baxter's diatribes against the current use of hypothesis was that of a chagrined divine, basically opposed to the new philosophy, those members of the Royal Society who sought an end to disputation in science (just as the Restoration promised mitigation of theological and political disputes) also were concerned about hypotheses. Samuel Parker, Bishop of Oxford, and fellow of the Royal Society, wrote in his *A Free and Impartial Censure of the Platonick Philosophie*:

I am lately grown such a desparing *Sceptick* in all *Physiologicall* [i.e. concerned with the structure of matter] *Theories,* that I cannot concern my self in the Truth or Falshood of any *Hypotheses.* For though I preferre the Mechanicall Hypotheses before any other, yet me thinks their contexture is too slight and brittle to have stresse laid upon them; and I can resemble them to nothing better then your *Glasse drops* from which if the least portion be broken, the whole *Compages* immediately dissolves and shatters into Dust and Atoms; for their parts which rather lie then hang together being supported only by the thin filme of a brittle Conjecture (not annexed by experience and observation) if that fail anywhere, the whole Systeme of the Hypothesis unavoidably shatters.[3]

Parker's views were very characteristic of his fellows of the Royal Society: though the mechanical philosophy may be preferable to the Aristotelian, still it rests on a tenuous basis. In order to transcend the hypothetical nature of this philosophy, resort to experience must be made, as Bacon taught.

[1] *Reasons*, p. 495. See also Baxter, *The Nature and Immortality of the Soul* (London, 1682).
[2] Baxter, *Reasons,* p. 498.
[3] Samuel Parker, *A Free and Impartial Censure of the Platonick Philosophie* (Oxford, 2nd ed., 1667), p. 46. Henceforth cited as *Censure.*

We can expect from the Royal Society, Parker continued, a great improvement in natural philosophy, 'for they having discarded all particular *Hypotheses*, and wholly addicted themselves to exact Experiments and Observations, they may not only furnish the World with a compleat *History of Nature*, (which is the most useful part of *Physiologie*) but also lay firm and solid foundations to erect Hypotheses upon, (though perhaps that must be the work of future Ages).' It was the task of the Royal Society, Parker maintained, to forgo theory and return to experiment and observation with a view to completing the task begun by Bacon, that of instituting complete natural histories. Only on this foundation could hypotheses ever be securely founded. The constructing or framing of hypotheses must (if it is ever to be done) be the task of future generations:

[A]t least we shall see whether it be possible to frame any certain *Hypotheses* or no, which is the thing I most doubt of, because, though the *Experiments* be exact and certain, yet their application to any *Hypotheses* is doubtfull and uncertain; so that though the *Hypothesis* may have a firm *Basis* to bottome upon, yet it can be fastned and cemented to it no other way, but by conjecture and uncertaine (though probable) applications.[1]

Surely this was a Baconianism of a radical sort; Bacon, raised from the dead, might echo Marx and deny that he was a Baconian! Parker, in placing authority in the experiment alone, distrusted all inference from it. Science, to Parker, must be confined (in its substance) to systematization and rude classification, although it may employ 'the handsomest and most probable *Hypotheses* for delight and Ornament'.[2]

Parker was very concerned with method; he understood, as did many of his colleagues, that it was a new method that they themselves were forging. It was because of this methodological concern that Parker rejected the hypothetical physics. 'For tis not enough', he insisted, 'to prove that this or that is the Idea of any thing, because some fanciful men are able to make pretty *Hypotheses* concerning it'.[3] However, like those of many scientifically-minded theologians of the Royal Society, Parker's philosophical concerns were not strictly internal. He, too, was anxious lest the new mechanism injure traditional Christianity.

In a book written in 1681, *A Demonstration of the Divine Authority of the Law of Nature and the Christian Religion*, Parker censured the 'Plebeans and Mechanicks [who] have philosophised themselves into Principles of

---

[1] Parker, *Censure*, p. 47. The term 'to frame an hypothesis' was often used before Newton's famous *Hypotheses non fingo*; this usage lends credence to the translation of Newton's *Hypotheses non fingo*, or 'I do not frame hypotheses.'
[2] Ibid., p. 48.
[3] Ibid., p. 67.

Impiety'.[1] As many were, Parker was above all an anti-Hobbist, opposing the mechanical philosopher particularly over his insistence that 'all the contrivances of the minds of Men are nothing but the mechanical Results of Matter and Motion'.[2] Against this position, Parker posed a rational faith in Divine Providence:

[T]he folly and nonsense of meer Mechanism or accounting for the nature of Thinges onely by Matter or Motion or any other second Causes is so notorious, that all the Philosophers in the World never were, nor ever will be able to give any the least account how so much as a Stone should fall to the ground without a Divine Providence.[3]

Into this company, Parker would welcome Glanvill, Barrow, Henry More, Cudworth, and many others.

Of all the early fellows and publicists of the Royal Society, Joseph Glanvill is perhaps the best example of the reaction against the hypothetical physics. He put his arguments so concisely and well, that it is perhaps best once again to let the author speak for himself:

We have [Glanvill wrote to Lady Margaret, Duchess of Newcastle] yet no certain theory of Nature, and in good earnest, Madam, all that we can hope for, as yet, is but the History of thinges as they are, but to say how they are, to raise general *Axioms,* and to make *Hypotheses,* must, I think, be the happy privilege of succeeding Ages . . . [W]e have yet no such thing as Natural Philosophy; Natural History is all we can pretend to.[4]

Like Parker, therefore, Glanvill despaired (at least for the present) of any scientific theory; all that can now be attained is natural history, after the fashion of Bacon.

Yet Glanvill did, in fact, initially incline towards the mechanical philosophy, if only as an antidote to Aristotelianism, although aware of its limitations. In the *Scepsis scientifica* of 1665, Glanvill commended Descartes, and actually seemed to accept the principles of the hypothetical physics:

And though the Grand Secretary of Nature, the miraculous Des-Cartes, hath here infinitely out-done all the Philosophers who went before him, in giving a particular and *Analytical* account of the *Universal Fabrick*: yet he intends his principles but for *Hypotheses,* and never pretends that things are really or necessarily as he hath supposed them: but that they may be admitted pertinently to solve the

---

[1] Samuel Parker, *A Demonstration of the Divine Authority of the Law of Nature and the Christian Religion* (London, 1681), p. iii. Henceforth cited as *Demonstration.*
[2] Ibid.
[3] Parker, *Demonstration,* p. xi.
[4] Joseph Glanvill to Lady Margaret, Duchess of Newcastle, in *Letters and Poems Written in Honour of the Incomparable Princess Margaret, Duchess of Newcastle* (London, 1676), p. 124.

Phaenomena, and are convenient supposals for the *use of life.* Nor can any further account be expected from humanity, but how things possibly *may have been made* consonantly to sensible nature: but infallibly to determine how *they truly were effected,* is proper to him only that saw them in the *Chaos,* and fashion'd them out of that confused *mass.* For to say the *principles* of Nature must needs be such as out *Philosophy* makes them is set bounds to *Omnipotence,* and to confine infinite power and *wisdom* to our shallow *models.*[1]

This statement of Glanvill is extremely important, and effort at careful study of it will be amply repaid. It is obvious that Glanvill is echoing the views of Descartes on what has here been called the 'hypothetical physics'. All that natural philosophers can hope for is to frame hypotheses concerning 'how things possibly *may have been made*'; these hypothetical constructions are conveniences in solving the phenomena and for practical purposes. Glanvill has accepted both mechanism and hypothesis.

Again in 1671 Glanvill rose to the defense of the mechanical philosophy. Answering Baxter's diatribes, Glanvill maintained that the 'experimental and mechanick' school was the best partisan for the greater glory of God.[2] It is true that a 'Modern Sadducee [Hobbes] pretends that all things we do are performed by *meer* matter and *motion* and consequently that there is no such thing as an immaterial being.'[3] But most of the new corpuscularians, Glanvill continued, deny such atheistic tenets; Gassend, Descartes, and Boyle, for example, all admit the existence of an immaterial soul. 'Thus far I dare say I may undertake for most of the *Corpuscularian Philosophers* of our times, excepting *those* of Mr. Hobb's way.'[4]

By 1676, however, Glanvill became less enthusiastic, and returned to what he thought to be a closer adherence to Baconian empiricism. In an essay 'Against Confidence in Philosophy and Matters of Speculation', Glanvill's scepticism clearly emerged:

Our *best natural* Knowledg is *imperfect,* in that, after all our confidence *Things still are possible to be* otherwise: *Our Demonstrations* are raised upon *Principles* of our *own,* not of *Universal* Nature; And as my Lord *Bacon* notes, we *judg* from the analogy of our *selves, not* the *Universe . . .*

We cannot, Glanvill claimed, philosophize in confidence, for

[T]he *best Principles of natural* Knowledg in the World are but *Hypotheses,* which *may be,* and *may be otherwise . . .* The *ways* of God in *Nature* (as in *Providence*) are not

---

[1] Joseph Glanvill, *Scepsis scientifica* (London, 1665), pp. 211–12.
[2] Joseph Glanvill, *Philosophia pia* (London, 1671), p. 22. Henceforth cited as *Philosophia.*
[3] Ibid., p. 33.   [4] Ibid., p. 109.

as *ours* are: Nor are the Models that we frame any way commensurate to the vast-ness and profundity of his Works; which have a *depth* in them greater than the *Well of Democritus*.[1]

Similarly, in an essay 'Of the Modern Improvements of Useful Know-ledge', Glanvill warned that

[*Y*]*oung Philosophers* must take care of looking on their *Systematick Notions* as the *bounds* and *perfections* of *Knowledge*; nor make account to *fix eternally* upon *those Theories,* as *establish'd* and *infallible Certainties* but consider them in *the modest sense* of *Hypotheses,* and as things they are to take in their passage to *others* that are more *valuable* and *important*.[2]

The 'more *valuable* and *important*' things of which Glanvill was writing were, of course, new empirical observations. In a sense, Glanvill did not depart in substance from his earlier view of the role of hypothesis, merely in emphasis. By 1676 Glanvill was concerned about the disciples of the great mechanical philosophers who (the disciples), disregarding the teaching of their masters, began to look upon the great systems as certain and true. Opposed to this sect, Glanvill advocated a return to pristine Baconianism as he saw it. In an essay entitled 'Anti-fanatical Religion and Free Philo-sophy, in a Continuation of the New Atlantis', Glanvill described the new men of Solomon's House:

They did not set down any *System* or *Body of Principles* as *certain* and *established*: They consider'd the *incomprehensible* wisdom that is in *the works of God*; . . . and therefore gave but *timerous* assent to any notions in *Natural Philosophy*: They held no *infallible* Theory *here*: Nor would they allow any speculations or accounts of Nature to be more then *Hypothesis* and probably conjecture . . . So that they thought with much reason, that best *Foundation* for *Natural Philosophy* would be a good *History of Nature*: This they saw to be very defective in their Time.[3]

These diligent searchers into nature, Glanvill continued, were avid students of Descartes and Gassend, however they did not adhere to the mechanical philosophy 'as the *certain* account of Nature; nor yielded their assent as to *positive* and *establish'd* Truth; but entertain'd what they thought *probable,* and *freely dissented* in other matters'.[4]

Glanvill characterized the prevailing mood of the Royal Society in these brief essays. Attracted by the ingenious hypotheses, sceptical of the hypo-thetical method, the fellows of the Royal Society were receptive to alter-native paths in seeking out the secrets of nature. Trusting only in the

---

[1] Joseph Glanvill, *Essays on several important subjects in philosophy and religion* (London, 1676), p. 15. Henceforth cited as *Essays*.
[2] Ibid., p. 55.　　　　　　　　　　　　　　　　　　[3] Ibid., p. 48.
[4] Glanvill, *Essays,* p. 50.

'certainty' of experience, some (the 'empirics') retreated into the anti-theoretical, natural-historical citadel, much encouraged by the scepticism of Glanvill and Parker. Others, like Henry Power, followed Boyle in attempting to illustrate by experiment the plausibility of the hypotheses of Descartes and Gassend.[1]

It is perhaps paradoxical that Robert Boyle, while a culture-hero to the extreme empirics or vulgar Baconians, was not of that party. He was, to be sure, a critic of the more obvious excesses of the hypothetical physicists. He retained, however, a position *vis-à-vis* hypothesis which tasted of their influence. By wishing to bring the mechanical philosophy within the compass of the experimental learning, Boyle was attempting to mediate between those who denied the utility of theorizing and those who denied the practicability of any experimental knowledge of corpuscles and their motions.

Boyle's relation to the hypothetical physics is both interesting in its own right, and important for the understanding of the relationship between the mechanical philosophy, and its methodological offspring, the hypothetical physics. It should be remembered that opponents of the hypothetical physics rarely doubted the utility or truth of the basic tenets of the mechanical philosophy, i.e. that matter and motion are fundamental to the phenomena of nature.

Boyle wrote little which addresses itself directly to the problem of the role of 'hypothesis' (in the sense current during the early Restoration period); perhaps the best indication of his attitude is the collection of experimental essays in which he attempted to justify the reasonableness of mechanical, corpuscular hypotheses.[2]

Boyle did, however, write a short essay on the subject of hypothesis, an essay which remained unpublished until recently when three versions of it have appeared.[3] 'The Requisites of a Good Hypothesis' drawn from the Royal Society's Boyle papers, is a fascinating example of Boyle's attempt to utilize and yet transcend the current practice of supplying hypotheses to explain natural phenomena. Boyle's requisites for a *good* hypothesis is strikingly similar to that of Descartes and Hobbes. A good hypothesis, in short, must be self-consistent, contain no absurdities, be sufficient to explain the phenomena and consistent with them, i.e. it must not contradict any known physical truth.[4] But Boyle did not remain content merely with

---

[1] See above, Chapter IX.   [2] Ibid.

[3] Slightly different versions have been published in Richard Westfall, 'Unpublished Boyle Papers Relating to Scientific Method', *Ann. Sci.* **12** (1956) 63–73, 107–17, esp. pp. 116–17, and Marie Boas Hall, *Robert Boyle on Natural Philosophy* (Bloomington, Indiana, 1965), pp. 134–5.

[4] Hall, *Boyle on Natural Philosophy*, pp. 134–5.

a *good* hypothesis; he sought to improve upon the standards of the hypothetical physicists. Characteristically, his improvements lay primarily in the area of experimental confirmation.

An *excellent* hypothesis, according to Boyle, must have auxiliary proofs, be simple and concise, be the unique or most reasonable explanation, and, most importantly, must enable the natural philosopher to predict future phenomena. An important characteristic of an excellent hypothesis, Boyle wrote, is

That it enable a skilful Naturalist to foretell future Phaenomena by their Congruity or Incongruity to it; and especially the events of such Experiments as are aptly devis'd to examine it, as Things that ought or ought not, to be consequent to it.[1]

It was not the framing of mechanisms over which Boyle differed with Hobbes, Gassend and Descartes, nor was it over the *utility* of hypotheses (which he believed to be great). Boyle primarily objected to the practice of the hypothetical physicists of not attempting to *confirm* their insights through experimentation. The extreme democracy of some of the hypothesizers, regarding all speculations as having equal weight, was clearly unacceptable. For Boyle, in short, hypotheses were useful, speculative insights into nature which required further confirmation via experiment in order to be received into natural philosophy.[2]

Systematization was, however, not anathema to Boyle as it was to some of his Royal Society colleagues. Hypotheses and their systematic organization was useful, perhaps even necessary, but the resulting superstructure had to be recognized as temporary, depending for longevity upon its agreement with future experiments.

I would have [Boyle wrote] such superstructures looked upon only as temporary ones; which though they may be preferred before any others, as being the least imperfect, or, if you please, the best in their kind that we yet have, yet are they not entirely to be acquiesced in, as absolutely perfect, or uncapable of improvement.[3]

Whereas Boyle, like his continental counterpart Christian Huygens, wished primarily to improve and renovate the contemporary use of hypotheses in natural philosophy, Isaac Barrow and Isaac Newton aimed at

[1] Ibid., p. 135.
[2] For a good examination of Boyle's and Newton's philosophy, especially with regard to hypotheses, see Maurice Mendelbaum, *Philosophy, Science, and Sense Perception* (Baltimore, 1964).
[3] Boyle, *Works,* I, 303.

ending it.[1] Barrow, and more potently, his successor Newton, attempted no less than a reform of natural philosophy. The goal of this reform was the end of vain disputation over equally unascertainable hypotheses, and the introduction of *certainty* in science through experiment and mathematics. It is this remarkable reform, which altered the face of science so markedly, which we must now examine.

[1] Robert Hooke, who deserves more than a brief footnote, was another late seventeenth-century scientist who attempted to renovate the hypothetical method by observation and experiment. See, especially, the preface to the *Micrographia* (London, 1665) and the *Posthumous Works,* ed. Richard Waller (London, 1705). See also below, Chapter XI.

XI
ATOMISM AND THE YOUNG NEWTON

IF CHARLETON, Boyle, and others promoted the reception of atomism by ridding it of its atheistic taint, and Boyle advanced it by attempting to bring it within the compass of experimental learning, it was left for Isaac Newton to utilize atomism as the conceptual background for his principles, thereby bringing it to bear upon mathematical physics. To say that Newton incorporated atomism into his natural philosophy is somewhat bold, for Newton aimed at higher generality, and in a precise sense his mathematical principles in no way depend upon any theory of matter. Yet it is abundantly clear, as it has often been observed, that Newton was in some sense an advocate of the atomic philosophy.[1] It is the purpose of this chapter to illustrate in just which manner Newton was such an advocate.

Newton's published statements regarding atomism are ambiguous; they leave some doubt as to the extent to which Newton insisted upon any specific theory of matter. His hesitancy with respect to atomism, and reluctance to subscribe to particular mechanisms have led to confusion among historians of science regarding the exact nature of his views. This confusion can only be clarified by an investigation of Newton's *method* in historical perspective, for the limitations set by his concept of *scientific rigour* defined the nature and extent of his commitment to atomism.

Newton was profoundly influenced by Isaac Barrow's conception of mathematical physics, and by Francis Bacon's quest for certainty in science through experiment. Bacon's experimentalism found fertile soil in the Royal Society, which was, on the whole, delighted with efforts to illuminate nature through experiment. Unfortunately, the Baconians of the Royal Society were often 'vulgar empirics', merely groping in the dark and ignoring Bacon's admonishment first to 'light a candle'.[2] Barrow and Newton, on the other hand, combined Baconian experimentalism with a reverence for mathematical and quantitative technique which enabled them to interpret Bacon in a new light and in a more sophisticated manner. From considerations of method, Bacon abandoned Greek atomism; Newton,

---

[1] See A. J. Snow, *Matter and Gravity in Newton's Physical Philosophy* (London, 1926), *passim*; Marie Boas and A. R. Hall, 'Newton's Mechanical Principles', *J. Hist. Ideas* **20** (1959) 167–78; S. I. Vavilov, 'Newton and the Atomic Theory', in *Royal Society Newton Tercentenary Celebrations* (Cambridge, 1947), pp. 43–55; Henry Guerlac, *Newton et Epicure* (Paris, Palais de la Découverte, 1963), *passim*; Alexandre Koyré, *Newtonian Studies* (Cambridge, Mass., 1965), *passim*.

[2] Bacon, *Works*, VIII, 115; see above, Chapter X.

however, attempted to show how aspects of atomism could be made certain through experiment, proceeding in a consciously Baconian fashion, but with a Baconianism far more complex than that of most of his contemporaries.

It was Isaac Barrow who initiated a search for a new path to certainty in science by blending theory and experiment. Reinforced by his own mathematical competence, Barrow looked to experiment to add the necessary links with experience. His early discourse against Cartesianism was obviously inspired, in part, by Bacon;[1] the reverence which 'Verulamus' commanded was earned primarily on methodological grounds. Barrow never fell, however, into the blind empiricism of some of his contemporaries.

Barrow's conception of physics is crucial for the understanding of that of Newton, for Barrow was one of the formative scientific influences upon the mind of the young Newton.[2] There were others, of course, including Bacon, Boyle, Henry More, Descartes, Gassend, and Charleton.[3] Fortunately, Newton's notebook from his student days at Cambridge survives, and delineates quite clearly the nature of his early interests.

The manuscript entitled '*Quaestiones quaedam Philosophicae*', dating from about 1664, is centrally concerned with problems of the mechanical philosophy. Basically Newton sided with the atomists in positing atoms and void. He transcribed a long section 'Of the First Mater [*sic*]' which he quoted from Walter Charleton's *Physiologia*.[4] 'It remaines therefore', he concluded, 'that the first matter must be attomes'.[5]

Another authority from whose work Newton quoted was Henry More. Having attacked pagan Epicureanism, More contributed to the purification of atomism in his *Immortality of the Soul* and several lesser works. More admitted the existence of 'indiscerpible' or indivisible particles. Unlike the mechanical philosophers, however, he also admitted the existence of *incorporeal causes*. In this, More went far beyond Charleton and the others who merely wished to remove atheistic implications from the mechanical philosophy. Not only did More insist upon the immateriality of the soul, but also attempted to integrate spiritual essences into natural philosophy. Matter, according to More, is dead and inert. It is *spirit* which, penetrating

[1] Isaac Barrow, *Theological Works,* ed. Alexander Napier (Cambridge, 1859), IX, 86.
[2] Cf. D. T. Whiteside, 'Isaac Newton: Birth of a Mathematician', *Notes Rec. R. Soc. Lond.* (1964) 53–62. Whiteside shows that Newton was not Barrow's pupil in the formal sense, and implies that Barrow was not an intellectual influence upon the young Newton.
[3] Richard Westfall, 'The Foundations of Newton's Philosophy of Nature', *Br. J. Hist. Sci.* I (1962) 172–3.
[4] Cambridge University Add. MSS. 3996, fol. 88. Henceforth cited as *Newton, MSS.* See also Charleton, *Physiologia*, p. 107.
[5] *Newton, MSS.*, fol. 89.

9

and uniting with matter, causes it to move.[1] The notion of spiritual cause is one which greatly impressed Newton; it was to reappear later many times in his thought.

With respect to method, the primary influences upon the young Newton were unquestionably those of Francis Bacon and of Isaac Barrow. In a section entitled 'Philosophy [Occult Qualityes]' Newton held, with Bacon, that:

The nature of things is more securely and naturally deduced from their operations out upon another and upon our senses. And where by the former experiments we have found the nature of bodys, by the latter we may more clearly find the nature of the senses.[2]

Newton's approach to the mechanical philosophy in the *Quaestiones* already showed the marks of a new (and still Baconian) approach. Newton began to investigate mechanical principles using springs and weights, needles on corks in water, and magnetic pendula.[3] His aim, even in this early work, was a quantitative understanding of nature; from this approach he hoped to gain certain knowledge regarding mechanical principles.

In all probability, the influence of Isaac Barrow was strong even in the *Quaestiones*; in Newton's later reluctance to 'feign hypotheses' it is unmistakable. In 1665–6, Barrow delivered a series of mathematical lectures in which can be found a clear statement of what later came to be known as Newton's 'mathematical way'.[4]

Barrow came to grips with the central issue confronting the physics of his day: the 'hypothetical physics' practised so widely was inconsistent with the present needs of natural philosophy. For example, in the present state of physics, '[I]t is hard to imagine distinctly, and define exactly what is *Colour* in Physics . . . because we have seldom any clear Notion of [it].'[5] What do the mechanical philosophers offer but *ad hoc* hypotheses?

And for the Dispatch of every Question [Barrow stated] or the Explication of a Phaenomenon, a new and distinct Hypothesis is invented. From whence it happens that in what is called and accounted the same Science are found Hypotheses without number.[6]

The mechanical philosophy, to be sure, is true and useful in so far as it is based upon matter and motion,[7] but who is fooled by the elaborate dreams of the systematizers?

---

[1] Henry More, *Collection of Several Philosophical Writings* (London, 1662), pp. 36, 43–47, *et passim*.

[2] *Newton MSS.*, fol. 101 v.   [3] Ibid., fols. 94–102.

[4] See Edward Strong, 'Newton's Mathematical Way', *J. Hist. Ideas* **12** (1951) 90–110.

[5] Isaac Barrow, *Mathematical Lectures Read in the Publick Schools,* trans. John Kirby (London, 1734), p. 54. Henceforth cited as *Mathematical Lectures*.

[6] Ibid., p. 61.   [7] Ibid., p. 21.

No Body surely is so simple or credulous, as immediately to agree or force himself to acquiesce with any of these *Hypotheses* (though ingeniously devised) not only as true but as at all possible or in any degree probable.[1]

Hypothetical physics had left natural philosophy sterile and unproductive. Barrow had, however, a programme to extricate it from this unfortunate situation, a programme later to be followed by his pupil Newton. The model, according to Barrow, was to be 'divine Archimedes'.[2] The plan was to combine the rigour of mathematics and the certainty of experiment into that synthesis for which Bacon had called in his *Novum Organum*.

The foundations of theory, Barrow maintained, must be in experimentation in order to arrive at a 'certain Science'.[3] Combined with it must be the potency of mathematics, powerful enough even to compute 'immense Hills of Atoms'.[4] Mathematics cannot be divided into theoretical and practical; it is, and must be, both.[5] Through experimentation and mathematical analysis Barrow hoped to reach his goal, which was to achieve a certain science and an end to degrading disputation so common in natural philosophy.

Especially [Barrow stated] since my Endeavours are for no other end but that by disputing I may utterly eradicate and remove all Causes of Disputation, weighing as far as I am able the Reason of Things in the Ballance of Experience.[6]

This programme became the hallmark of Isaac Newton's method: to weigh 'the Reason of all Things in the Ballance of Experience', and thereby to eradicate disputation and uncertainty from natural philosophy. Furthermore, Newton would be, as Barrow urged, a *mathematical* philosopher.

[Mathematicians] only meddle with such Things [Barrow claimed] as are certain, passing by those that are doubtful and unknown. They profess not to know all Things, neither do they affect to speak of all Things. What they know to be true, and can make good by invincible Arguements, that they publish. . . .[7]

The above quotation could serve as a description of Newton's course of action, with certain exceptions, in the years following.

Newton's reluctance to publish a systematic theory of matter or to dispute about the mechanical causes of phenomena was not, therefore, merely the result of timidity, inordinate fear of dispute, or innate reticence, although

---

[1] Barrow, *Mathematical Lectures*, p. 58.   [2] Ibid., p. 59.
[3] Ibid., p. 133.
[4] Ibid., p. xxix. It is interesting that Barrow wrote (p. 53) of the 'Mathematical Way of learning'.
[5] Ibid., p. 50.   [6] Ibid., p. 239.
[7] Ibid., p. 64.

these may have been contributing factors. It was primarily an essential part of a programme to transform natural philosophy from the 'hypothetical physics' of Descartes, Gassend, and Hobbes to a new, certain science. Newton was never a mechanical philosopher in the same manner as Descartes, Huygens, or Hobbes, although, to be sure, he did not deny the ultimate existence of mechanical causes. Even on this issue he was not adamant, and was disposed to admit spiritual causes after the fashion of Henry More.[1]

Newton's atomism took this form: he accepted atoms and the void, principles which he took to be indisputably supported by experience. Beyond these two, all knowledge had to be educed cautiously from experiment. This procedure is in evidence in all his published writings, and in many of his unpublished manuscripts.

The manuscripts recently published by A. R. and M. B. Hall afford excellent examples of Newton's 'mathematical way'. The *De Gravitatione et Aequipondio Fluidorum*, attributed to the period 1664–8, or shortly after Barrow's mathematical lectures, clearly outlines the path Newton was to follow in almost all his published scientific writings. Presumably following Barrow's admonition, he saw himself as a *mathematician*, one who meddles only with things that can be made certain. Newton was attempting to be, not a new Descartes, but a new Archimedes. He wrote in the *De Gravitatione*:

To the extent that [the science of gravity and equilibrium of fluids] appertains to the mathematical sciences, it is reasonable that I largely abstract from physical considerations. . . . [I]n order, moreover, that its usefulness may be particularly apparent, and the certainty of its principles perhaps confirmed, I shall not be reluctant to illustrate the propositions abundantly from experiments as well.[2]

Newton was stating here his role as a mathematical physicist, and outlining his relationship to experiment. After defining the elements of his physical system (force, inertia, conatus, velocity, hard and elastic bodies, etc.), Newton explained his procedure. 'And thus I have accommodated these definitions not to physical things but to mathematical reasoning, after the manner of the Geometers who do not accommodate their definitions of figures to the irregularities of physical bodies.'[3]

Turning to Newton's 'Baconianism' and its relation to his theory of matter, a striking example can be found in his manuscript *De Aere et Aethere*,

[1] See *Newton MSS.*, fol. 113; Isaac Newton, *Unpublished Scientific Papers*, ed. A. R. and M. B. Hall (Cambridge, 1962), pp. 138–9, 353. Henceforth cited as *Unpublished Papers*.
[2] Newton, *Unpublished Papers*, p. 121.   [3] Ibid., pp. 151–2.

probably written in the period 1673–5. In the *De Aere*, Newton investigated the phenomenon of repulsion, marshalling his evidence in a fashion strongly reminiscent of Bacon. In order to prove the existence of repulsive forces, Newton first listed five instances of the rarefaction of air near bodies.[1] Next, he presented six examples illustrating the tendency of bodies to avoid contact. Newton was concerned solely with the properties of the phenomenon itself and refused to speculate about the causes which he knew to be disputable. He listed several possible opinions: the repulsive force may be caused by an aether, by an incorporeal spirit or by a repulsive atmosphere surrounding a body.

Many opinions [he wrote] may be offered concerning the cause of this repulsion. The intervening medium may give way with difficulty or not suffer itself to be much compressed. Or God may have created a certain incorporeal nature which seeks to repel bodies and make them less packed together. Or it may be in the nature of bodies not only to have a hard and impenetrable nucleus but also [to have] a certain surrounding sphere of most fluid and tenuous matter which admits other bodies into it with difficulty. About these matters I do not dispute at all. . . .[2]

There were certain conclusions which Newton was willing to make.

But as it is equally true that air avoids bodies and bodies repel each other mutually, I seem to gather rightly from this that air is composed of the particles of bodies torn away from contact and repelling each other with a certain large force.[3]

'Upon this foundation', Newton wrote, 'all the properties of air are easily understood'.[4] This foundation consisted merely in the assertion that air consists of particles which by some indefinite mechanism were mutually repulsive. From this 'experimentally' educed basis, he proposed to explicate the properties of air. For example, the assertion that the volume of air is reciprocally proportional to the pressure applied to it (which according to Newton 'Hooke proved by experiment') is explicable only if the possibility that the particles of air are in mutual contact is rejected. If, however, the particles are forced apart by 'some principle acting at a distance',[5] the law is easily explained. If the distance between the centres of two bodies is doubled, Newton continued, the repulsive force will be halved, and if trebled, the force will be decreased to one third its original potency. Hence 'by an easy computation', the expansion of air is seen to be reciprocal to that

---

[1] Newton, *Unpublished Papers*, p. 221.
[2] Ibid., p. 223. Paragraph crossed out in the original manuscript.
[3] Ibid., p. 223.   [4] Ibid., p. 223.
[5] Ibid., p. 223.

distance.[1] Similarly, the 'mystery' of the expansion of the air by heat is easily explained. When heat agitates the component particles of the air, the mutually repulsive forces between particles cause increased distances between them.[2]

In the *De Aere* Newton has utilized Bacon's natural history method by first collecting instances, and then educing general principles from them. He has, however, added Barrow's insistence upon a quantitative procedure to it, by demonstrating with some success that the phenomenon now known as Boyle's Law and which Newton called 'Townley's Hypothesis' can be explained assuming a repulsive force varying inversely with distance.

A comparison of Newton's treatment of the air in the *De Aere* with that of Descartes underlines the difference between Newton's approach to natural philosophy and that of the hypothetical physicists. In the fourth part of his *Principia philosophiae*, entitled 'Of the Earth', Descartes discussed why air can easily be expanded and contracted. Air, he claimed, is composed of small particles which are very soft 'as small feathers or the ends of very delicate strings'.[3] These pliant, feather-like particles are by their very nature easily moved, and consequently the volume which they occupy is easily expanded and contracted. This explanation, though brief, is a good example of the hypothetical method. Descartes had no way of *knowing* whether his ingenious model was, in fact, true. But it was consistent with the facts, as far as it went, and was also consistent with the rest of his own system. These requirements being satisfied, Descartes rested, assured that his explanation, even if it could not be proved true, equally could not be proved false.

Newton on the other hand made stricter requirements upon scientific explanation. Proceeding from the phenomena, Newton assumed axioms from which he could derive the quantitative properties. To be sure, Newton was leaving the qualitative physics of Descartes, and entering the realm of quantitative physics. But he was doing more. He was abandoning the hypothetical method, and embracing the path to certainty in science advocated by Barrow.

Newton's first optical paper, published in the *Philosophical Transactions* for February 1672, is a more sophisticated example of Newton's 'Baconian method'.[4] In it Newton described his famous prism *experimentum crucis*.

[1] Newton, *Unpublished Papers*, p. 224. See also Newton's *Principia Mathematica*, book II, prop. XXIII for a proof.
[2] Ibid., pp. 224–5.   [3] Descartes, *Oeuvres*, III, 368–70.
[4] Some discussions of this paper include Thomas Kuhn, 'Newton's Optical Papers', in Newton, *Papers and Letters on Natural Philosophy*, ed. I. B. Cohen (Cambridge, Mass., 1958), pp. 27–45, henceforth cited as *Papers and Letters*; Richard Westfall, 'Newton's Reply to Hooke and the Theory of Colour', *Isis* 54 (1963) 82–96; and Johannes Lohne, 'Newton's "Proof" of the Sine Law and his Mathematical Principles of Colours', *Archs Hist. exact Sci.* 1 (1961) 389–405.

The notion of an *experimentum crucis* is derived from Bacon. In the *Novum Organum* (book II, aphorism XXXVI) Bacon described what he termed the *Instantias crucis* or 'instance of the signpost'. The term *experimentum crucis* has often been translated 'crucial experiment', thus obscuring its Baconian origins. The term *'crucis'* or 'of the signpost' refers to the signs directing the traveller in his choice between two possible paths. Bacon's *Instantias crucis* was an experience which eliminated certain possibilities from consideration by pointing out the proper path. In his *Micrographia*, Robert Hooke altered Bacon's phrase to *experimentum crucis* while discussing an experiment relating to Des Cartes' theory of colours. 'This Experiment', Hooke wrote, 'therefore will prove such a one as our *thrice excellent Verulam* calls *Experimentum Crucis,* serving as a Guide or Land-mark, by which to direct our course in the search after the true cause of Colours'.[1] It is, in all probability, this passage to which Newton referred when he labelled his experiment an *experimentum crucis.*

The inferences which Newton drew from his experiment are in accord with the dicta laid down, in this case, by Bacon. In Newton's eyes, his conclusions were certain because educed rigorously from experience. In addition to several statements regarding the nature of colour, and its 'connate' relationship with light, Newton also suggested 'no nor perhaps' that the experiment proved that light itself is a *substance* rather than a *quality.*[2]

As is well known, Hooke, Pardies, Huygens, and others quickly responded to Newton's paper with letters of their own criticizing Newton's theory. Ignatius Pardies, a French Jesuit, was one of the first to reply, discussing what he called 'Mr. Newton's very ingenious hypothesis of light and colours'.[3] It was, of course, Newton's purpose to avoid disputations over 'hypotheses' and in his answer to Pardies of 13 April 1672, he stated:

I do not take it amiss that the Rev. Father calls my theory an hypothesis, inasmuch as he was not acquainted with it. But my design was quite different, for it seems to contain only certain properties of light which, now discovered, I think easy to be proved, and which if I had not considered them as true, I would rather have them rejected as vain and empty speculations than acknowledged even as an hypothesis.[4]

His own conclusions, Newton insisted, were not part of the hypothetical physics of so many of his contemporaries; they were true and certain properties of light proved by induction from experience. Newton's point

---

[1] Robert Hooke, *Micrographia* (London, 1665), p. 54.
[2] Newton, *Papers and Letters,* p. 57. See Richard Westfall, 'Newton and his Critics on the Nature of Colours', *Archs int. Hist. Sci.* **15** (1962) 47–58, for a different point of view.
[3] Newton, *Papers and Letters,* p. 86.   [4] Ibid., p. 92.

would be obvious to those familiar with the exhortations of Barrow, but Pardies, nursed in the physics of his day, apologized in his reply without giving any indication that he understood Newton's objection. In his second reply to Pardies, Newton expostulated at length upon his reaction against hypothetical physics:

[I]t is to be observed that the doctrine which I explained concerning refraction and colours, consists only in certain properties of light without regarding any hypotheses by which those properties might be explained. For the best and safest method of philosophizing seems to be, first to inquire diligently into the properties of things, and establishing those properties by experiments and then to proceed more slowly to hypotheses for the explanation of them. . . . For if the possibility of hypotheses is to be the test of truth and reality of things, I see not how certainty can be obtained in any science.[1]

The last sentence is the crucial one, for it points to the very heart of Newton's method. The hypothetical physics of Descartes, Hobbes, Gassend, *et al.* permitted no certainty. Bacon had rejected Greek natural philosophy for reasons similar to those of Newton, and the lack of certainty in contemporary physics was the object of Barrow's strictures. Newton's method outlined in the above quotation is virtually that of Bacon, properly understood. Robert Hooke, however 'Baconian' he might have been, did not understand Newton's point.

Hooke's critique of Newton's theory clearly demonstrates his lack of appreciation of the proposed Newton-Barrow-Bacon reform of physics. '[A]s to his hypothesis of solving the phenomaena of colours thereby', Hooke wrote, 'I confess I cannot see any undeniable argument to convince me of the certainty thereof.'[2] Hooke, always thinking in terms of the mechanical philosophy, saw the essence of Newton's theory in his hint that light is a corporeal substance, and insisted that the same phenomena can be explained by his own hypothesis as by Newton's. Newton's theory is not necessarily incorrect, Hooke explained, and is indeed a 'very subtil and ingenious' hypothesis, although not necessarily the only one.[3]

Newton was incensed. Hooke had missed the entire point of what he was trying to accomplish. He confessed his disappointment in Hooke's approach, for he found Hooke 'somewhat more concern'd for an *Hypothesis*, than I expected'.[4] His own theory, Newton stressed, was not a mere hypothesis. It is true, he conceded, that he argued on the basis of experiments for the corporeity of light, 'but I do it without any absolute positiveness, as the word *perhaps* intimates; and make it at most but a very plausible

---

[1] Newton, *Papers and Letters*, p. 106.   [2] Ibid., p. 111.
[3] Ibid., p. 114.   [4] Ibid., p. 116.

consequence of the Doctrine and not a fundamental part of it.'[1] Many mechanical hypotheses could be conjured up to explicate the truths which he had found; he himself offered one. But he again stressed 'I do not think it needful to explicate my Doctrine by any *Hypothesis* at all.'[2] Barrow had wished to end vain disputation over hypotheses; Newton echoed his call and insisted: 'You see therefore how much it is besides the business at hand to dispute about *Hypotheses*.'[3]

Newton faced much the same difficulty in the objections posed by Christian Huygens, who was in all probability the greatest scientist of that time. Huygens clung to the mechanical philosophy, insisting in regard to colours that '[T]ill he hath found this *Hypothesis* (of the mechanical origin of colours) he hath not taught us what it is wherein consists the nature and difference of Colours, but only this accident (which certainly is very considerable) of their *different Refrangibility*.'[4] In a reply of 3 April 1673, Newton once again explained his position:

But to examine how Colours may be explain'd *hypothetically* is besides my purpose. I never intended to shew wherein consists the Nature and Difference of colours, but only to shew, that *de facto* they are Original and Immutable qualities of the Rays which exhibit them; and to leave it to others to explicate by Mechanical Hypotheses the Nature and Difference of these qualities. . . .[5]

Newton's method might have been more obvious to his contemporaries had not an important passage of his original letter to Oldenburg been omitted in the final printing in the *Philosophical Transactions*. In the original Newton clearly explained his dissatisfaction with the hypothetical physics and outlined his quest, similar to that of Bacon, for certainty through experiment:

A naturalist [Newton wrote in the original] would scarce expect to see the science of those [colours] become mathematicall, yet I dare affirm that there is as much certainty in it as in any other part of Opticks. For what I shall tell concerning them is not an Hypothesis but most rigid consequence, not conjectured by barely inferring 'tis thus because not otherwise or because it satisfies all phaenomena' (the Philosophers universall Topick) but evinced by the meditation of experiments concluding directly & without any suspicion of doubt.[6]

In the above quotation, Newton made an explicit attack upon the principles of the hypothetical physics, attempting to replace it with a physics based directly upon experimentation.

[1] Newton, *Papers and Letters*, p. 118. [2] Ibid., p. 123.
[3] Ibid., p. 123. [4] Ibid., p. 136.
[5] Ibid., p. 144.
[6] Isaac Newton, *Correspondence*, ed. H. W. Turnbull (Cambridge, 1959–61), I, pp. 96–7.

How, then, is one to treat the detailed and hypothetical mechanisms outlined by Newton in his famous letter to Boyle?[1] Newton's reservations in that letter should, perhaps, be given more weight than is commonly done. Newton made no pretence of holding the views expressed there in any firm fashion.

I have [Newton wrote] so long deferred to send you my thoughts about the Physicall qualities we spoke of, that did I not esteem my self obliged by promise I think I should be ashamed to send them at all. The truth is my notions about things of this kind are so undigested that I am not well satisfied myself in them, & what I am not satisfied in I can scarce esteem fit to be communicated to others, especially in natural philosophy where there is no end of fansying.[2]

Reluctantly, however, Newton was persuaded by Boyle to speculate on mechanisms employing an aether. Was this hesitancy mere coyness or was Newton genuinely concerned about the proper mode of philosophizing? In the light of his previous consistent statements, it appears that the latter was indeed the case. 'For my own part', Newton concluded, 'I have so little fansy to things of this nature that had your encouragement not moved me to it, I should never I think have thus far set pen to paper about them.'[3] Newton's speculations in the letter to Boyle are doubtlessly of historical interest; to dignify them as a *theory of matter* is to go beyond Newton's own intent.

The point which has been stressed concerning the relationship of Newton's method to the existing manner of natural philosophy need no longer be laboured. Newton's 'theory of matter' in the light of this method has still to be examined. What was Newton's attitude toward atomism and to which view of the structure of matter did he adhere? The evidence points to the supposition that Newton assumed, as was by then generally accepted, the existence of atoms in a void. This view of matter is discernible in the background of the *Principia,* although the work is couched in more general terms.

That Newton was thinking of an atomic structure of matter when writing the *Principia* is made evident by the manuscripts relating to the work. In the draft preface (written 1687) Newton wrote that he 'suspected' that all phenomena depended upon the attractive and repulsive forces by which the particles of bodies are reciprocally moved. The mechanism of the forces he admitted to be unknown. That interatomic forces exist we can presume from an extrapolation process:

For if Nature be simple and pretty conformable to herself causes will operate in the same kind of way in all phenomena, so that the motions of smaller bodies

---

[1] Newton to Boyle, 28 February, 1679, in *Correspondence,* II, 288–95.
[2] Ibid., p. 288.   [3] Ibid., 295.

depend upon certain smaller forces just as the motions of larger bodies are ruled by the greater force of gravity. It remains therefore that we inquire by means of fitting experiments whether there are forces of this kind in nature, then what are their properties, quantities and effects.[1]

To investigate these microscopic forces Newton held to be part of the future programme of physics.

The draft *Conclusio* also originally intended for the first edition of the *Principia*, and likewise omitted, continued this approach, and even echoed the words of the draft preface manuscript. It is unlikely that both were meant to be published simultaneously. In the *Conclusio* Newton relied solely upon particles and their attractive and repulsive forces, the mechanism of which he left undetermined. We can learn of the existence of atomic forces, Newton held, through reasoning by analogy:

Whatever reasoning holds for greater motions should also hold for lesser ones as well. The former depend upon the greater attractive forces of larger bodies, and I suspect that the latter depend upon the lesser forces, as yet unobserved, of insensible particles. . . .[2]

Newton suppressed the *Conclusio* and the draft preface, both of which clearly accepted a particulate structure of matter (by 1687 a commonplace among natural philosophers), and which suggested that the particles act upon each other through a rapidly varying attractive force and a more slowly varying repulsive one.[3] Beyond these modest assumptions and their implications Newton did not wish to venture.

The modest 'theory of matter' of Newton was not very different in his own eyes from that of the ancient atomists. All that Newton insisted upon was this: bodies are composed of small, hard, equal particles endowed with motion in the void, and very probable associated with both attractive and repulsive forces. With the important exception of the *forces*, Newton's theory was virtually that of the atomists.

Much of the *Principia* can be, and was, viewed as presenting the mechanics of atomic motion,[4] although the work referred primarily to visible bodies. The gravity of gross bodies, for example, is said to be merely the compounded gravitational forces of their parts (book III, prop. VIII, theorem VII, cor. I). Moreover, in the face of strong Cartesian opposition, Newton insisted upon the existence of the vacuum. '*Itaque*', he wrote in book III, prop. VI, cor. III of the first edition, ' *Vacuum necessario datur.*' This very strong statement was weakened in the later editions where

---

[1] Newton, *Unpublished Papers,* p. 307.   [2] Ibid., p. 333.
[3] Ibid., p. 337.
[4] See Halley's review of the *Principia* in Newton, *Papers and Letters,* p. 408.

Newton wrote that 'if all the solid particles of all bodies are of the same density . . . then a void space or vacuum must be granted.'[1]

That Newton conceived of bodies in terms of their component particles is clear from his treatment of the attractive forces of bodies. In the *scholium* following proposition LXXXIV, problem XLIII of book I, Newton himself admitted that he was attempting to explain the laws of attraction in "bodies consisting in like manner of attractive particles".

In section XIII of book I, Newton dealt at length with the forces pertaining to 'particles of which an attractive body is composed'[2] and showed that the refraction of light could easily be explained on this basis.[3] Newton, therefore, treated the visible world as if composed of the void and equal corpuscles associated with attractive and, possibly, repulsive forces. Detailed mechanisms involving atoms or their forces were not, to be sure, ready for publication as part of natural philosophy, and could be dealt with only obliquely in the *Principia*.

How did Newton reconcile his adoption even in so modest a fashion of an admittedly unexperimental atomism with his strict rules of method? The answer was given in the draft preface and *Conclusio*, and in more complete form in the *Rules of Reasoning* which first appeared in the second edition.[4] The sentiments of the *Conclusio* and draft preface of the year 1687 are virtually those of Rule III (1713). The natural philosopher must, Newton maintained in explaining Rule III, extrapolate from sensible experiences to understand the workings of the submicroscopic particles which compose bodies. '[B]ecause we perceive extension in all that are sensible, therefore we ascribe it universally to all other bodies.'[5] Similarly, we learn by experience that sensible bodies are hard, and therefore 'because the hardness of the whole arises from the hardness of the parts, we . . . justly infer the hardness of the undivided particles not only of the bodies we feel but of all others'.[6] All the qualities of bodies of the visible world arise from the qualities of their component particles:

The extension, hardness, impenetrability, mobility and inertia of the whole, result from the extension, hardness, impenetrability, mobility and inertia of the parts, and hence we conclude the least particles of all bodies to be also extended and hard and impenetrable, and movable and endowed with their proper inertia. And this is the foundation of all philosophy.[7]

[1] Newton, *Principia Mathematica,* book III, prop. VI, th. III, 3rd ed. Henceforth cited as *Principia*. The Motte-Cajori translation has generally been followed.
[2] Ibid., book I, prop. LXXXVI, th. XLIII.
[3] Ibid., book I, prop. XCVI, th. L, and *scholium*.
[4] Alexandre Koyré, 'Les Regulae Philosophandi', *Archs int. Hist. Sci.* 13 (1960) 3–14.
[5] Newton, *Principia,* book III, rule III.
[6] Ibid.   [7] Ibid., book III, rule III.

It was in the above sense—that matter is composed of small, hard, impenetrable atoms endowed with motion and inertia—that Newton claimed that 'the system of Epicurus and Lucretius is true'.[1] The verification of this 'hypothesis' he found by inference from the structure and motions of sensible bodies. This extrapolation was, in his eyes, a Baconian induction from experience in the same sense that Bacon had not restricted his new method to gross bodies only, but in like manner extended its reach to invisible particles and spirits.

Newton's evolution after 1687, especially in the various editions of the *Opticks*, is a tortuous and complex problem, beyond the scope of this essay.[2] Let it suffice to note that Newton clearly distinguished between 'queries' as they appeared in the *Opticks*, and 'hypotheses'. A *query* represented a question to be decided by experiment; an *hypothesis* was the hallmark of that mode of philosophizing which was content with possible explanations.[3] As Newton himself pointed out in the advertisement to the second edition of the *Opticks,* he added 'questions', preferring that form of discourse because he was 'not yet satisfied about it for want of Experiments'.[4]

In the *Opticks,* Newton was committed still to mathematico-experimental philosophy. Samuel Clarke's preface to the first Latin edition, *Optice,* is particularly instructive. According to Clarke, in words anticipating the General Scholium of the second edition of the *Principia,* '*non fictibus Hypothesibus*', the natural philosopher can proceed to employ mathematical calculations and experiments.[5]

At any rate, the *Principia* marked a high point in the history of atomism; its appearance in 1687 denoted the full acceptability of atomism by the integration of its tenets into a work of mathematical physics. Thus Edmund Halley, whose review revealed that he regarded the *Principia* as, in part, the mechanics of atomism, was enabled to say in some 'queries' of 1693 that the tenets of '*Epicurean* and *Atomical* Philosophers . . . at present obtain in the world.'[6]

With Newton, the atomic philosophy reached its highest point of development in the seventeenth century. In so far as it was at all possible, Newton's atomism was grounded in experiment; at the very least it was consistent with the general rules of procedure laid down by Bacon, by

[1] Gregory's notes in Newton, *Correspondence,* III, 338.
[2] See Guerlac, *Newton et Epicure,* pp. 27–35; Guerlac, 'Francis Hauksbee, experimenteur au profit de Newton', *Archs int Hist. Sci.* **16** (1963) 124–8; A. Koyré, 'Les queries d l'Optique', *Archs int. Hist. Sci.* **13** (1960) 15–29.
[3] A. R. Hall and M. B. Hall, 'Clarke and Newton', *Isis* **52** (1961) 584.
[4] Newton, *Opticks* (London, 2nd ed., 1718), sig. A4 recto.
[5] Clarke, preface to Newton's *Optice* (London, 1706), sig. A2 recto.
[6] E. Halley, 'Some Queries concerning the Nature of Light and Diaphanous Bodies', *Phil. Trans. R. Soc.* **17** (1693) 998–9. Page 998 is misnumbered 999. Halley was here suggesting a system in which there existed qualitatively differing atoms.

Barrow, and by himself. He differed markedly from Boyle, for example, who was interested in illuminating the mechanical philosophy by demonstrating its experimental manifestations. In a strict sense, Newton was far more 'Baconian' than Boyle. The former attempted to reach a theory of matter inductively from experience; the latter attempted to explicate an existing theory by experimental demonstration, an endeavour completely in accord with similar previous attempts (on a smaller scale) by Gassend, Charleton, and others. Certainly Newton, in his atomism, was also in accord with the mandate for natural philosophy laid down by Barrow, for Newton's hard particles were treated mathematically and, as far as possible, with precision.

XII
EPILOGUE

By 1700 the adherents of atomism had prevailed over the obstacles which faced their predecessors in 1600. The obstacles—theological, experimental, and theoretical—were overcome in several ways. Some were cleverly circumvented, as in the case of the theological objections; some were battered down by frontal assault as in the case of the experimental and theoretical objections. By the end of the century the objectors no longer posed a serious threat. In 1600, atomism was a 'radical' philosophy, destructive of the still prevailing scholastic world-picture. By 1700, atomism as a mechanical philosophy was, in England, the conservative view.

Thomas Hariot, around 1600, had introduced atomism into his work as an hypothesis to aid in scientific explanation. He saw in the atomic doctrine a unifying approach for the explanation of certain experimental phenomena such as refraction, and for the overcoming of mathematical difficulties such as the problem of infinities. The effect of his use of atomism was twofold. First, he systematically attacked the Aristotelian mode of explanation, foreshadowing the objections of the later mechanical philosophers. Secondly, he stirred the ire of the philosophical and theological establishment by his use of the ideas of the ancient materialists. Hariot and the entire circle around the Earl of Northumberland were, however, politically vulnerable. For the reasons described above, the group's reticence about such a controversial matter was greatly increased;[1] its members published nothing relating to the atomic doctrine.[2]

Atomism failed to take root for other, internally compelling reasons. As Bacon pointed out at the time, the atomism of the Greeks was far too speculative to be of use to experimental philosophers. There were too few instances in which the doctrine proved of real worth. Hariot utilized it, to be sure, to explain problems of physical optics and to overcome difficulties in his mathematics. But his successes went unnoticed by most of his contemporaries and remained the exclusive property of his own scientific *avant-garde*. The opposition of Francis Bacon, on the one hand, and of the theologically conservative on the other, proved too strong for Hariot's atomism.

[1] See above, Chapters II and III.
[2] The sole exception was Nicholas Hill who published his views abroad in Paris.

When, however, atomism was reintroduced by Hobbes, Charleton, and the Newcastle Circle in the 1640s and 1650s, the situation was radically altered. The political-theological establishment which had insisted upon orthodoxy was rent by the strife of the civil war. A natural philosopher could now openly adhere to atomist and materialist views with relative impunity, as did Hobbes. Secondly, the later atomists were willing to 'purify' their views and bring them into accord with Christian orthodoxy. The neo-Epicureans of the 1650s, like Charleton and Evelyn, were pious Christians, eager to correct the errors of the pagans. Another major endeavour along these lines was the *True Intellectual System of the Universe* (1678) of Ralph Cudworth. According to Cudworth, the atomic philosophy was of theologically pure Mosaic origin; it was later 'atheized' by Democritus and Leucippus. Following Henry More, Cudworth held that belief in atomism and in the existence of *incorporeal* substances were not incompatible. He maintained, in fact, that immaterial substances are involved in cognition and sensation.[1] Finally, the experimental basis for the plausibility of atomism had broadened considerably in the thirty years after Hariot's death. Atomism became a powerful tool to render comprehensible and systematic many of the new endeavours involving the vacuum pump, the microscope, and Torricelli barometer. It was here that Boyle played his most important role; the corpuscular philosophy rapidly became a fashionable explanation for natural phenomena. The Baconians of the Royal Society were able, therefore, to consider atomism seriously whereas their famous predecessor had abandoned it.

In the 1650s, after the appearance of Gassend's work on the continent and Charleton's in England, atomism rapidly overcame the barriers erected for it. The men of Gresham College, predecessor of the Royal Society, were delighted with the systematic anti-Aristotelianism of the Epicurean atomist doctrine. The author of the 'Ballad of Gresham College' wrote:

> Thy Colledg, Gresham, shall hereafter
> Be the whole world's Universitie
> Oxford and Cambridge are our laughter
> Their learning is but Pedantry.
> These new Collegiates doe assure us
> Aristotle's an Asse to Epicurus.[2]

The spread of the mechanical philosophy manifested itself also in less lyrical fashion. In 1659 there was a serious suggestion that separate chairs in

[1] Ralph Cudworth, *True Intellectual System of the Universe*, ed. Thomas Birch (London, 1820), I, pp. 52–55, 124–5. For a brief survey of the concept of the Mosaic origin of atomism see Danton Sailor, 'Moses and Atomism', *J. Hist. Ideas* 25 (1964) 3–16.
[2] Quoted in Dorothy Stimson, *Scientists and Amateurs* (New York, 1948), p. 58.

Cartesian and Epicurean philosophy be established at Oxford and Cambridge.[1] Joseph Glanvill reported in an address to the Royal Society that '[S]ome of you (to whose excellent works the learned is deeply indebted), publickly own the Cartesian and Atomical Hypothesis.'[2] Henry Oldenburg, at the very heart of the early Royal Society, reflected in 1671 the satisfaction of that body in the *purified* atomic philosophy:

And if Modern diligence hath dived so deep as to find more satisfaction in *atoms,* then in the three controverted *Principles,* will *Diogenes Laertius,* or any other Historian, or Antiquary, allow these Criticks to call the *Atomical* the *New* Philosophy? Or have our Modern Atomists done amiss in purging the old atoms of *Greece* from the Heathenish Errors of *Greece*?[3]

The effort to free atomism from its ancient atheism was not accomplished, Oldenburg noted in a dedicatory epistle to Robert Boyle in 1670, without opposition:

And since a noyse hath been raised by temarious Answers against you [Boyle] as if you were too indulgent to the old *Atomists,* I hold myself bond in Justice to take publick notice . . . that you were . . . [not] deterr'd by the Heathenish mistakes about Atoms.[4]

Boyle's greatest contribution, according to Oldenburg, the confirmation of existing mechanical philosophies through experimentation:

I must continue to discourse of the Lord *Bacon, Gilbert, des Cartes, Gassendus,* and others the Miracles of modern and revived Philosophy . . [T]ruly 'tis to me very strange that several of these Excellent persons have so luckily espoused those *Hypotheses* of Nature in many true particulars which *You* [Boyle] have by manifest Experiments evinc'd and confirm'd as if . . . they had been guided by an Heavenly Ray to divine what would be the Result from diligent tryals.[5]

Boyle's 'diligent tryals' of the hypotheses of the mechanical philosophers were, for Oldenburg and for many other members of the Royal Society, the convincing tests of the systems of Descartes and the atomists. Henceforth who could doubt the existence of atoms or corpuscles?

With the publication of Newton's *Principia,* the doctrine of atomism itself entered upon a new stage. Newton's work had a twofold effect upon atomism. First, the doctrine was made secure in its acceptance by Newton's use of particle and void. As Samuel Clarke reported, Newtonian atomism

[1] R. F. Jones, 'Puritanism, Science and Christ Church', *Isis* **31** (1939) 65–67. See also Jackson Cope, 'Evelyn, Boyle, and Dr. Wilkinson's "Mathematico-Chymico-Mechanical School",' *Isis* **50** (1959) 30–2.
[2] Joseph Glanvill, *Scepsis Scientifica, or the Vanity of Dogmatizing,* ed. John Owen (London, 1885), p. liii.
[3] Henry Oldenburg, 'Preface', *Phil. Trans. R. Soc.* **6** (1671) 2089.
[4] Henry Oldenburg, 'Epistle Dedicatory to Boyle', *Phil. Trans. R. Soc.* **5** (1670) 1145.
[5] Ibid., p. 1145.

was regarded as superior to that of the Greeks because the latter 'knew not how to apply [matter and vacuum] by mathematics to the explication of the phenomena of nature'.[1] Secondly, by emphasizing the theoretical concept of *force*, Newton introduced an atomic quality which was taken by some as an *anti*-mechanical philosophical device. If atoms were the ultimate components of bodies, what was the mechanism of inter-atomic force?

Newton himself vacillated on this issue until, perhaps, 1717. In the unpublished *De Aere et Aethere*, Newton suggested three possible mechanisms, of which two were mechanical and one supposed that 'God may have created a certain incorporeal nature which seeks to repel bodies and make them less packed together.'[2] True to his method, Newton did not advance these hypotheses in any formal sense. But it is important to note that Newton has here permitted the possibility of a non-mechanical origin for forces, a possibility which the mechanical philosophers would not countenance. Newton remained faithful to this point of view in his third letter to Dr. Richard Bentley:

Gravity [Newton wrote in 1693] must be caused by an Agent acting constantly according to certain Laws; but whether this Agent be material or immaterial I have left to the Consideration of my Readers.[3]

Echoes of the letter to Bentley reappeared in the '*Quaestiones*' appended to the 1706 edition of Newton's *Opticks*, translated into Latin by Samuel Clarke. The reasons behind Newton's abandoning his reluctance to publish conjectures are too complex to unravel here. For whatever reasons he may have had, he did publish them and in the last query Newton hinted at a non-material cause for gravity while rejecting the aether:

And for rejecting such a medium we have the authority of those the oldest and most celebrated philosophers of Greece and Phoenicia who made a vacuum and atoms, and the gravitation of atoms the first principles of their philosophy; tacitly *attributing to the gravitational force some cause other than matter*.[4]

This willingness on the part of Newton to suggest the possibility of non-mechanical causes,[5] probably derived from his early interest in the philosophy of Henry More. It was More who was the major champion, *contra Hobbes*, of immaterial and incorporeal causes. Newton's early inclination toward a mechanical cause for gravity was balanced by this later awareness of the possibility and even desirability, of immaterial and incorporeal causes.

[1] Samuel Clarke in *Leibniz-Clarke Correspondence*, ed. H. G. Alexander (Manchester, 1963), p. 21. Henceforth cited as Clarke, *Correspondence*.
[2] Newton, *Unpublished Papers*, p. 223.
[3] Isaac Newton, *Papers and Letters*, p. 303
[4] Newton, *Optice*, trans. Samuel Clarke, p. 314. Emphasis supplied.
[5] See also the *Scholium generale* of the second edition (1713).

Newton's disciple, the theologian Bentley, exemplifies the new turn given atomism by More and by anti-Hobbists like Samuel Clarke. The discussion of gravity in Bentley's *Confutation of Atheism* (1693) clearly showed the characteristics of the new, anti-mechanical atomism.

'Tis utterly unconceivable [Bentley stated in a sermon delivered in December 1692] that inanimate brute Matter (without the mediation of some Immaterial Being) should operate upon and affect other Matter without mutual Contact; that distant Bodies should act upon each other through a Vacuum without the intervention of something else. . . .'[1]

Yet, Bentley continued, a vacuum *does* exist, and atoms *do* attract each other across it. No material effluvium or action of the medium transmits this gravitational attraction. Gravity, he insisted, is an influence which distant bodies exert upon each other through a void with no material or mechanical intermediary.[2] According to Bentley, gravitation is the result of a 'Divine energy' above all mechanism:

[W]e have great reason to affirm, That Universal Gravitation, a thing certainly existent in Nature, is above all Mechanism and material Causes, and proceeds from a higher principle, a Divine energy and impression.[3]

Dr. Samuel Clarke, another Newtonian theologian, held similar views on the ultimate non-mechanical cause of gravitation, despite his statements welcoming mechanical explanations for gravity (if such were possible).[4] Clarke argued, after the fashion of More, effectively for the existence of another type of cause, one incorporeal and immaterial. Echoing Bentley and Newton, Clarke wrote to Leibniz in 1716:

That one body should attract another without any intermediate means is indeed not a miracle but a contradiction. . . . But the means by which two bodies attract each other, may be invisible and intangible, *and of a different nature from mechanism*; and yet, acting regularly and constantly, may well be called natural. . . .

Clarke's position on gravity in the correspondence with Leibniz reflected an earlier stand taken in an interesting exchange of letters with Henry Dodwell. In the Dodwell letters, Clarke made an overt and specific attack upon the mechanical philosophy, claiming that the existence of an immaterial power of gravity was proved with 'Mathematical Certainty':

[T]he great Phaenomena of Nature [Clarke wrote] cannot possibly depend upon any *mechanical* Powers of Matter and Motion, but must be produced by the Force

[1] Richard Bentley, *Confutation of Atheism,* in Newton, *Papers and Letters,* p. 340.
[2] Ibid., p. 341.
[3] Ibid., p. 344.
[4] Clarke, *Correspondence,* p. 119.　　　　　[5] Ibid., p. 53. Emphasis supplied.

and Action of some higher Principle: And so leading us even with Mathematical Certainty to immaterial Powers.[1]

Clarke, therefore, explicitly advocated the existence of a non-material cause of gravity. In part, he rested his case upon the fact that gravitational force is proportional to *mass*, and independent of the surface area: thus, he reasoned, it could not be an impact phenomenon. Hence, Clarke concluded,

[I]f *material Impulse*, be not the Cause of Gravity; then some Being that is *not material* . . . must of Necessity be allowed to be the Cause of it.[2]

Dodwell's reply objected to the inclusion of non-mechanical efficient causes in nature, citing as an authority Robert Boyle.[3]

Bentley and Clarke, confident of Newton's support, utilized the phenomenon of gravity as an example of the interaction of God and the physical universe. In doing so, they sacrificed the fundamental tenet of the mechanical philosophy, that all causes in nature, after the divine gift of motion, were explicable in terms of the action of matter. The mechanical philosophy took revenge, however, on these ardent Newtonian theologians. The instrument of reprisal was, paradoxically, Isaac Newton.

The *Newsletter* of 19 December 1717, reported that 'Sir Isaac Newton has advanced something new in the latest edition of his Optics which has surprised his physical and theological disciples.'[4] The reason for the consternation of his disciples was Newton's sudden and unexpected reversal of his previous rejection (*Optice*, 1706) of the aether as a mechanical cause of gravitation. In the second English edition (1717) and in all later editions Newton systematically altered the older (1706) 'Queries' and added new ones, introducing the hypothesis of an elastic, active, rare, and subtile medium or aether.[5] In the newer version for example the ancient authorities of Greece and Phoenicia were 'tacitly attributing Gravity to some other Cause than *dense* Matter', thereby admitting the subtile aethereal medium as a mechanical cause.[6] In all cases in which Newton had in the earlier edition discussed the absence of *matter*, he now referred to the non-existence of *dense matter*, reserving special status for his aether.[7]

---

[1] Samuel Clarke, *Works* (London, 1738), III, 849. Emphasis supplied.
[2] Clarke, *Works*, III, 846.
[3] Ibid., III, 882.
[4] Historical Manuscripts Commission, *Portland Manuscripts* (Norwich, 1899), V. 550.
[5] See Henry Guerlac, 'Francis Hauksbee, experimenteur au profit de Newton', *Archs int. Hist. Sci.* 16 (1963) 124–8, and *Newton et Epicure* (Paris, Palais de la Découverte, 1963), pp. 27–35.
[6] Newton, *Opticks*, 4th ed. (New York, 1952), p. 369. Emphasis supplied.
[7] Ibid., pp. 349–50, 369, 374.

This obvious suggestion of a mechanical view of gravitation embarrassed his disciples Clarke and Bentley who had incorporated a non-mechanical gravity into theology as well as into physics. Was Bentley's 'Divine energy' and Clarke's 'higher Principle' to be reduced to mere matter, however subtile? Apparently Newton's last word held it to be so. Atomism in Newton, therefore, returned full circle to its seventeenth-century roots, remaining faithful to its origins as a mechanical explanation of natural phenomena.

SELECTED BIBLIOGRAPHY

THE following bibliography is not exhaustive; no bibliography involving so many major figures over an entire century could possibly be so. Many older studies, while pertinent, were omitted because they have been superceded by more recent works. A good bibliography of pre-1952 secondary literature was presented in Marie Boas, 'The Establishment of the Mechanical Philosophy', *Osiris* 10 (1952) 525–41. Miss Boas' bibliography is complementary to mine with respect to the older literature. I have grouped my bibliography into seven sections denoted by Roman numerals. Within each section, works are listed alphabetically by author, each work having its own Arabic numeral. A work pertinent to more than one section is cited, in sections following its first listing, by the Roman and Arabic numbers of its first citation.

I. INTRODUCTORY: THE HISTORY OF ATOMISM

1. CYRIL BAILEY, *The Greek Atomists and Epicurus* (Oxford, 1928).
   A standard work on the atomists of antiquity.
2. ERNST BLOCH, 'Die antike Atomistik in der neuern Geschichte der Chemie', *Isis* 1 (1913) 376–415.
   An interesting and still valuable study of the atomism of Sennert, Jungius, Boyle, and others.
3. MARIE BOAS, 'The Establishment of the Mechanical Philosophy', *Osiris* 10 (1952) 412–541.
   An ambitious attempt to depict the rise of the mechanical philosophy, stressing the 'original' contributions of Boyle. There are fundamental flaws in this early work; the role of Boyle is exaggerated; the role of Gassend is reduced; Hobbes is completely omitted; Bacon is misrepresented. The work has had, however, an enormous influence.
4. MARIE BOAS (HALL), 'Matter in the 17th Century', in *The Concept of Matter*, ed. Ernan McMullin (Notre Dame, Ind., 1963), pp. 344–67.
   Distinguishes between seventeenth-century 'scientists' and 'philosophers'.
5. CHARLES DAUBENY, *An Introduction to the Atomic Theory* (Oxford, 1831).
   Includes a long section on Roger Boscovich, but is inadequate on the seventeenth century.
6. CORNELIS DE WAARD, *L'expérience barométrique* (Thouars, 1936).
   An excellent example of the history of science as it should be written. Contains important material on early seventeenth-century atomism.

7. E. J. Dijksterhuis, *The Mechanization of the World Picture* (Oxford, 1961).
   Particularly good on seventeenth-century physics. Contains a useful survey of the theory of Aristotelian *minima*.

8. *Encyclopédie,* Lausanne, 1781.
   The article 'Epicuréisme' is particularly interesting on forgotten French disciples of Gassend.

9. J. C. Gregory, *A Short History of Atomism from Democritus to Bohr* (London, 1931).
   Poor.

10. G. D. Hadzsits, *Lucretius and his Influence* (New York, 1935).
    The literary influence of Lucretius in the sixteenth century.

11. Charles Harrison, 'Ancient Atomists and English Literature of the Seventeenth Century', *Harvard Studies in Classical Philology* 45 (1934) 1–79.
    Interesting and valuable account of the atomism revival in English literature. Contains material on Charleton.

12. Friedrich Lange, *History of Materialism,* trans. E. C. Thomas, 3 vols. (London, 1890–2).
    Rather unhistorical account by a nineteenth-century philosopher.

13. Kurd Lasswitz, *Geschichte der Atomistik vom Mittelalter bis Newton,* 2 vols. (Hamburg, 1892).

14. L. Mabilleau, *Histoire de la philosophie atomistique* (Paris, 1895).
    Good on Islamic and medieval sources.

15. Thomas Mayo, *Epicurus in England* (1650–1725) (Dallas, 1934).
    Interesting work, but weak on the history of the early period, and on the scientific applications of atomism. Suffers from incomplete familiarity with the primary sources.

16. J. R. Partington, *History of Chemistry,* vols. 2 and 3 only (London, 1961–2).
    Encyclopedic but uncritical. Good for bibliography.

17. J. R. Partington, 'The Origins of the Atomic Theory', *Ann. Sci.* 4 (1939) 245–82.
    Unreliable, particularly on Bacon.

18. Gaston Sortais, *La philosophie moderne depuis Bacon jusqu'à Leibniz,* 2 vols. (Paris, 1922).
    Excellent survey including balanced studies of Gassend, Bacon, and Hobbes.

19. G. B. Stones, 'The Atomic View of Matter in the XVth, XVIth and XVIIth Centuries', *Isis* 10 (1928) 445–65.
    Sketchy summaries of major and minor figures pieced together to resemble an historical article.

20. Andrew van Melsen, *From Atomos to Atom* (New York, 1960).
    Not very good on the seventeenth century, but has interesting material on medieval *minima* theory.

II. Introductory: Science and Society
in Tudor and Stuart England

1. John Aubrey, *Brief Lives*, ed. Andrew Clark, 2 vols. (Oxford, 1898).
    Lively, gossipy biographies by a seventeenth-century figure. Contains material on Hariot, Pell, Warner, Cavendish, Hobbes, Petty, and many others.
2. *Biographia Britannica*, 6 vols. (London, 1747–66).
3. *Biographia Britannica*, 2nd ed., 5 vols. (London, 1778–93).
    Contains detailed biographies of many important figures. The second edition is much enlarged, but goes from A to F only.
4. Ralph Blake, Curt Ducasse, and Edward Madden, *Theories of Scientific Method: the Renaissance through the 19th Century* (Seattle, 1960).
    A stimulating collection of essays. Particularly interesting on Descartes and Hobbes.
5. Marie Boas, *Scientific Renaissance* (New York, 1962).
6. C. D. Broad, 'The New Philosophy: Bruno to Descartes', *Canb. hist. J.* **8** (1945) 36–54.
    Good but very brief.
7. Harcourt Brown, *Scientific Organizations in 17th Century France* (Baltimore, 1934).
    Still the most important work in this crucial area.
8. Harcourt Brown, 'The Utilitarian Motive in the Age of Descartes', *Ann. Sci.* **1** (1936) 182–192.
    Brief analysis of continental utilitarianism in the age of Descartes.
9. Douglas Bush, *English Literature in the Early 17th Century*, 2nd ed. (Oxford, 1962).
    Valuable primarily for its excellent bibliography.
10. Douglas Bush, *Science and English Poetry* (New York, 1960).
    Of peripheral interest.
11. George Clark, *Science and Social Welfare in the Age of Newton*, 2nd ed. (Oxford, 1948).
    Clark's book is interesting and informative, but the need for work in this important area is great.
12. A. C. Crombie, 'The Scientific Revolution of the 17th Century and its Consequences', *Contemp. Phys.* **1** (1960) 220–9.
    Brief discussion of the impact of the major figures.
13. Mark Curtis, *Oxford and Cambridge in Transition: 1588–1642* (Oxford, 1959).
    Interesting, readable account. Presents a too spirited defence of the universities as centres of scientific activity.
14 Herbert Dingle, 'Essential Elements in the Scientific Revolution of the 17th Century', *Actes du VIIᵉ Congrès International d'Histoire des Sciences*, ed. F. S. Bodenheimer (Jerusalem, 1953), pp. 272–8.
    The impact of dynamics on seventeenth-century thought. Little new.

15. RENÉ DUGAS, *Mechanics in the Seventeenth Century*, trans. Freda Jacquot (Neuchatel, 1958).
Brief accounts of various scientists. Very poor translation makes the book almost unreadable.

16. MARGARET ESPINASSE, 'The Decline and Fall of Restoration Science', *Past and Present* 14 (1958), pp. 71–92.
An examination of the decline of the image of science as reflected in literature.

17. A. R. HALL, *From Galileo to Newton, 1635–1720* (New York, 1963).

18. A. R. HALL, *The Scientific Revolution (1500–1800)* (London, 1954).
Hall's earlier book is preferable to the later.

19. WALTER HOUGHTON, 'The English Virtuoso in the 17th Century', *J. Hist. Ideas* 3 (1942) 51–73.

20. WALTER HOUGHTON. 'History of Trades: Its Relation to 17th Century Thought', *J. Hist. Ideas* 2 (1941) 33–60.
Both articles are valuable essays in important areas.

21. F. R. JOHNSON, 'Gresham College: Precursor of the Royal Society', *J. Hist. Ideas* 1 (1940) 413–438.
More work needs to be done on Gresham College despite Johnson's valuable article.

22. RICHARD FOSTER JONES, *Ancients and Moderns*, 2nd ed., (St. Louis, 1961).

23. WILBUR JORDAN, *The Development of Religious Toleration in England,* vol. 2 (Cambridge, Mass., 1936).
Good account of religious problems in the period under discussion.

24. ANNELIESE MAIER, *Die Mechanisierung des Welthilds im 17, Jahrhundert* (Leipzig, 1938).
Brief work, discussing major figures such as Galileo and Descartes, and such minor ones as Kenelm Digby.

25. STEPHEN MASON, 'Science and Religion in 17th Century England', *Past and Present* No. 3 (1953), pp. 28–74.
Concentrates on Puritanism, Calvinism, and science.

26. KATHERINE MAYNARD, 'Science in early English Literature (1550–1650)', *Isis* 17 (1932) 94–126.
Includes material on Cavendish and Pell.

27. MARIN MERSENNE, *Correspondence,* ed. Cornelis de Waard, 7 vols. (Paris), 1932–8.
An excellent source of letters of scientific personalities in the early and mid-seventeenth century.

28. ROBERT MERTON, 'Science and the Economy of 17th Century England', *Science and Society* 3 (1938) 3–27.

29. ROBERT MERTON, 'Science, Technology and Society in 17th Century England'. *Osiris* 4 (1938) 360–632.
The *Osiris* article is an important one, dealing with the inter-relationships of science, capitalism and the Protestant ethic.

30. PAUL MOUY, *Le développement de la physique cartésienne* (1646–1712) (Paris, 1934).
Still the best book on Cartesian physics. Overstresses the Cartesianism of Huygens.

31. JAMES MULLINGER, *Cambridge Characteristics in the 17th Century* (London, 1867).
Sparse and of limited utility.

32. MARTHA ORNSTEIN, *The Role of Scientific Societies in the 17th Century* (Chicago, 1913).
Still valuable and unreplaced after 50 years.

33. JEAN PELSENEER, 'Gilbert, Bacon, Galilée, Kepler, Harvey et Descartes: leurs relations', *Isis* **17** (1932) 171–208.
An attempt to demonstrate the links between the scientific giants.

34. PETER RAMSEY, *Tudor Economic Problems* (London, 1963).
Essays on sixteenth-century economic problems. The latest and best for the general reader.

35. R. P. STEARNS, 'The Scientific Spirit in England in Early Modern Times (*c.* 1600)', *Isis* **34** (1943) 293–300.
Valuable study of pre-Baconian scientific interests.

36. DOROTHY STIMSON, 'Amateurs of Science in 17th Century England', *Isis* **31** (1939) 32–47.

37. DOROTHY STIMSON, 'Puritanism and the New Philosophy in 17th Century England', *Bull. Inst. Hist. Med. Johns Hopkins Univ.* **3** (1935) 321–34.
Brief essays, lacking penetration.

38. R. H. TAWNEY, *The Agrarian Problem in the Sixteenth Century* (London and New York, 1912).
A monumental study of sixteenth-century economics.

39. E. G. R. TAYLOR, *Mathematical Practitioners of Tudor and Stuart England* (Cambridge, 1954).
Has a good bibliography.

40. HENRY VAN LEEUWEN, *The Problem of Certainty in English Thought: 1630–90* (The Hague, 1963).
Provocative study but lacks breadth and historical insight into seventeenth-century science.

41. RICHARD WESTFALL, *Science and Religion in 17th Century England* (New Haven, 1958).

42. ANTHONY À WOOD, *Athenae Oxonienses,* ed. Philip Bliss, 4 vols. (London, 1812–20).
Valuable biographies, although often unreliable, of Oxonians by a seventeenth-century author.

III. ATOMISM AND 16TH CENTURY ENGLAND
(CHAPTERS I, II)

1. XENIA ATANASSIEVITCH, *La doctrine metaphysique et géometrique de Bruno* (Paris, 1923).
An excellent summary of several of Bruno's atomistic works.

2. JOHN AUBREY, see above II, 1.

3. JOHN BAKELESS, *The Tragicall History of Christopher Marlowe,* 2 vols. (Cambridge, Mass., 1939).

4. G. R. BATHO, 'The Library of the Wizard Earl: Henry Percy, Ninth Earl of Northumberland', *Library* **15**, 5th series (1960), 246–61.
   Describes the library of Percy.

5. G. R. BATHO, 'Percy at Petworth (1574–1632)', *Sussex Archaeological Collections* **95** (1957) 2–27.
   Henry Percy and his house.

6. M. C. BRADBROOK, *The School of Night* (Cambridge, 1936).
   Miss Bradbrook thinks that *Love's Labours Lost* is about Ralegh and Hariot.

7. GERALD BRENAN, *History of the House of Percy,* 2 vols. (London, 1902).
   A history of an exciting family.

8. FRIEDRICH BRIE, 'Deismus und Atheismus in der englischen Renaissance', *Anglia* **48** (1928) 54–98, 165–8.
   Contains valuable material on religion in late sixteenth-century England.

9. *British Museum* Birch Manuscripts 4458; Additional Manuscripts 6782.
   Manuscripts by Thomas Hariot and Nathanael Torporley which discuss Hariot's atomism.

10. GIORDANO BRUNO, *Opera Latina,* ed. F. Tocco and H. Vitelli, 3 vols. in 8 parts (Florence, 1879–91).

11. GEORGE BUCKLEY, *Atheism in the English Renaissance* (Chicago, 1932).
    Contains material on Hariot, Marlowe, and their friends.

12. *Cambridge University* Additional Manuscripts 3996.
    Isaac Newton's notebook from his student's days.

13. JOHN CHAMBERLAIN, *Letters,* ed. Norman McClure, 2 vols. (Philadelphia, 1939).
    The letters of an associate of Percy.

14. ARTHUR COLLINS, *Peerage of England, Supplement,* 2 vols. (London, 1736).
    Contains biographical matter concerning Charles Cavendish.

15. A. C. CROMBIE, ed., *Scientific Change* (New York, 1963).
    Has several interesting articles but none which specifically relates to seventeenth-century atomism.

16. JOHN DEE, *Autobiographical Tracts,* ed. James Crossley (Chetham Society, 1851).
    Little of scientific interest.

17. JOHN DEE, 'Mathematical Preface', to Euclid, *Elements of Geometrie,* trans. H. Billingsley (London, 1570).
    The most important of Dee's extant scientific writings.

18. JOHN DEE, *Private Diary,* ed. J. O. Halliwell (London, 1842).

19. EDWARD DE FONBLANQUE, *Annals of the House of Percy,* 2 vols. (London, 1887).
    Informative, but uncritical.

20. THOMAS DIGGES, 'Perfit Description of the Coelestiall Orbes', ed. F. R. Johnson, *Huntington Library Bulletin* No. 5 (1934), pp. 83–95.

21. DIOGENES LAERTIUS, *Lives of Eminent Philosophers*, trans. R. D. Hicks (London, 1925).
   Used by many in the sixteenth and seventeenth centuries as introductions to Democritus and Epicurus.

22. Ecole practique des hautes études, *La science au seizième siècle* (Paris, 1960).
   Contains an article by Michel on Bruno's atomism as well as several other interesting essays.

23. WILLIAM GILBERT, *De Mundo nostro sublunari Philosophia Nova* (Amsterdam, 1651).

24. WILLIAM GILBERT, *On the Loadstone*, trans. P. Fleury Mottelay, n.p. (1892).

25. JOSEPH GLANVILL, *Scepsis Scientifica, or the Vanity of Dogmatizing*, ed. John Owen (London, 1885).

26. E. GOSSE, *Life and Letters of John Donne*, 2 vols. (London, 1899).

27. NICHOLAS HILL, *Philosophia Epicurea, Democritiana, Theophrastica propositer simpliciter non edocta* (Paris, 1601).

28. Historical Manuscripts Commission, *Calendar of State Papers Domestic 1603–10* (London, 1857).

29. R. HOOYKAAS, 'Experimental Origin of Chemical Atomic and Molecular Theory before Boyle', *Chymia* 2 (1949) 65–80.
   Claims that the atomic revival had root in chemical experimentation.

30. IRVING HOROWITZ, *The Renaissance Philosophy of Giordano Bruno* (New York, 1952).
   Bruno from the Marxist point of view. A somewhat forced interpretation.

31. F. R. JOHNSON, *Astronomical Thought in Renaissance England*, Baltimore (1937).
   A classic in the history of science. Still the best in its area.

32. F. R. JOHNSON, 'The Influence of Thomas Digges on the Progress of Modern Astronomy in 16th Century England', *Osiris* 1 (1936) 390–414.

33. F. R. JOHNSON, 'Thomas Digges, the Copernican System and the Idea of the Infinity of the Universe in 1576', *Huntington Library Quarterly* No. 5 (1934) 69–117.
   Classic articles by the 'discoverer' of Digges.

34. F. R. JOHNSON and SANFORD LARKEY, 'Robert Recorde's Mathematical Teaching and the Anti-Aristotelian Movement', *Huntington Library Bulletin* No. 7 (1935), pp. 59–87.

35. BEN JONSON, *Works*, ed. W. Gifford and F. Cunningham, 9 vols. (London, 1875).

36. W. J. KING, *The Natural Philosophy of William Gilbert and his Predecessors* (Washington, D.C., 1959).

37. PAUL KOCHER, *Science and Religion in Elizabethan England* (San Marino, California, 1953).
   Has much valuable material about Hariot and his friends, although all of it is obtainable elsewhere.

38. PAUL KOCHER, 'The Old Cosmos: Elizabethan Science and Religion', *Huntington Library Quarterly* 15 (1952) 101–21.
   Kocher's book is an expanded version of the article.

39. PAUL KRISTELLER, *Renaissance Thought* (New York, 1961).
Excellent essays in the history of renaissance thought. Kristeller's essay on renaissance Aristotelianism is particularly valuable.

40. EDMUND LODGE, *Portraits of Illustrious Personages of Great Britain,* vol. 5 (London, 1835).
Good brief biography and portrait (by Van Dyck) of Henry Percy.

41. GRANT McCOLLEY, 'Gilbert and Bruno', *Ann. Sci.* 2 (1937) 353–4.

42. GRANT McCOLLEY, 'Nicholas Hill and the *Philosophea Epicurea*', *Ann. Sci.* 4 (1939) 390–405.
McColley attempts to make Hill important.

43. JOHANNES MAGIRUS, *Physica Peripatetica* (Frankfurt, 1597).
An important Aristotelian text, undeservedly neglected by historians of science.

44. PAUL-HENRI MICHEL, *La cosmologie de Giordano Bruno* (Paris, 1962).
Good systematic study, including a long section on his atomism.

45. NICHOLAS OF CUSA, *The Idiot* (London, 1651).
An anonymous translation of an important and influential work.

46. GEORGE PEELE, *Works,* ed. A. H. Bullen, 2 vols. (London, 1888).

47. ANGELO PELLEGRINI, 'Giordano Bruno at Oxford', *Huntington Library Quarterly* 5 (1942) 303–16.
A brief examination of the evidence concerning Bruno's visit.

48. HENRY PERCY, *Advice to his Son,* ed. G. B. Harrison (London, 1920).
The advice of Percy gives some clues to his views on education and science.

49. HENRY PERCY, *Household Papers,* ed. G. R. Batho (London, 1962).
Contains important evidence concerning the formation of the Northumberland Circle.

50. SCIPION DU PLEIX, *Corps de philosophie* (Geneva, 1645).
A Peripatetic text.

51. PETER RAMSEY, see above II, 34.

52. ALEXANDER READ, *Chirurgicall Lectures of Tumors and Ulcers* (London, 1635).
The testimony of Hariot's physician.

53. ELEANOR ROSENBERG, 'Giacopo Castelvotro: an Italian Publisher in Elizabethan London and his Patrons', *Huntington Library Quarterly* 6 (1943) 119–45.
Percy was one of his patrons.

54. JOHN SHIRLEY, 'The Scientific Experiments of Sir Walter Ralegh, the Wizard Earl and the Three Magi in the Tower: 1603–17', *Ambix* 4 (1949) 52–66.
A mine of interesting and exciting material, but unfortunately ill-refined.

55. DOROTHEA SINGER, 'The Cosmology of Giordano Bruno (1548–1600)', *Isis* 33 (1941) 187–96.
A rather elementary approach.

56. DOROTHEA SINGER, *Giordano Bruno: His Life and Thought* (New York, 1950).
A prosaic but still valuable account.

57. DOROTHY STIMSON, *The Gradual Acceptance of the Copernican Theory of the Universe* (New York, 1917).
This book is sometimes unreliable.

58. E. A. STRATHMANN, 'John Dee as Ralegh's Conjuror', *Huntington Library Quarterly* **10** (1947) 365–72.
The author attempts to show that Dee may have been Ralegh's conjuror so roundly condemned in the sixteenth century.

59. E. A. STRATHMANN, *Sir Walter Ralegh* (New York, 1951).

60. E. A. STRATHMANN, 'Sir Walter Ralegh on Natural Philosophy', *Modern Language Quarterly* **1** (1940) 49–61.
From Strathmann's presentation one can conclude that Ralegh did not share Hariot's scientific views.

61. R. H. TAWNEY, see above II, 38.

62. HENRY VIETS, 'The *De Staticis Experimentis* of Nicolaus Cusanus', *Ann. med. Hist.* **4** (1922) 115–35.
Contains a translation of Cusa's *De Staticis*. Otherwise very prosaic.

63. ANTHONY À WOOD, see above II, 42.

64. FRANCES YATES, *A Study of Love's Labours Lost* (Cambridge, 1936).
Miss Yates claims that Shakespeare's play concerns Percy and Hariot rather than, as Miss Bradbrook claims, Ralegh and Hariot. Miss Yates presents a valuable Percy manuscript as an appendix.

65. EDGAR ZILSEL, 'The Origins of William Gilbert's Scientific Method', *J. Hist. Ideas* **2** (1941) 1–32.
Rather sketchy attempt to link Gilbert with his time.

IV.   THOMAS HARIOT AND HIS FRIENDS
(CHAPTERS III, IV)

1. JOHN AUBREY, see above II, 1.

2. H. P. BAYON, 'Circulation in MSS. before 1628', *Proc. R. Soc. Med.* **32** (1939) 707–18.

3. H. P. BAYON, 'William Harvey, Physician and Biologist', *Ann. Sci.* **4** (1939) 329–89.
Laudatory accounts of Harvey and 'refutations' of claims for precursors such as Warner. Bayon cannot even decide on a spelling for Warner.

4. *Biographia Britannica*, see above II, 2 and II, 3.

5. *British Museum* Additional Manuscripts 6784, 6788, 6789. Hariot manuscripts.

6. FLORIAN CAJORI, 'A reevaluation of Harriot's *Artis Analyticae Praxis*', *Isis* **11** (1928) 316–24.
Attempts to minimize Hariot's contributions to the theory of equations on the basis on his published book alone.

7. GEORGE CHAPMAN, *Poems*, ed. Phyllis Bartlett (New York, 1941).

8. GEORGE CHAPMAN, *Works,* ed. R. H. Shepherd, 3 vols. (London, 1885).

9. GALILEO GALILEI, *Dialogues Concerning Two New Sciences*, trans. Henry Crew and Alfonso de Salvio (New York, 1914).

10. R. T. GUNTHER, *Early Science at Oxford,* vol. 1 (Oxford, 1923).
Gunther is an historical compiler. Here he has compiled one or two titbits about Hariot.

11. JAMES O. HALLIWELL, *A Collection of Letters Illustrative of the Progress of Science in England from the Reign of Queen Elizabeth to that of Charles the Second* (London, 1841).

12. THOMAS HARIOT, *A Briefe and True Report of the New Found Land of Virginia* (London, 1588).
A fascinating report of Virginia and its inhabitants.

13. THOMAS HARIOT, *Artis Analyticae Praxis* (London, 1631).
Hariot's only published scientific work, edited and published by Warner and Aylesbury a decade after his death.

14. G. B. HARRISON, ed., *Willobie His Avisa* (London, 1926).
Contains valuable material relating to Hariot's reputation for impiety.

15. HELEN HERVEY, 'Hobbes and Descartes in the Light of the Correspondence between Sir Charles Cavendish and Dr. John Pell', *Osiris* 10 (1952) 67–90.
An excellent article utilizing much unpublished material.

16. Historical Manuscripts Commission, *Portland Manuscripts*, 2 vols. (London, 1892).
Contains Hobbes and Cavendish letters.

17. Historical Manuscripts Commission, *Salisbury Manuscripts*, vols. 17 and 18 (London, 1938–40).

18. DAVID JARDINE, *Criminal Trials,* 2 vols. (London, 1832).
Contains an account of Ralegh's trial.

19. JEAN JACQUOT, 'Thomas Harriot's Reputation for Impiety', *Notes Rec. R. Soc. Lond.* 9 (1952) 164–87.
The best account of Hariot's thought to date. Contains an important, hitherto unpublished Torporley manuscript.

20. JOHANN KEPLER, *Gesammelte Werke,* cd. Max Caspar, W. Von Dyck, and F. Hammer, 19 vols. (Munich, 1938–63).

21. JOHANNES LOHNE, 'Ballistik og bevegelseslaere pa Galileis tid', *Fra Fys. Verd.* No. 1 (1964) 1–4.
Contains much new material on Hariot's dynamics.

22. JOHANNES LOHNE, 'The Fair Fame of Thomas Harriott', *Centaurus* 8 (1963) 69–84.
An interesting account of the nineteenth century controversy over Hariot's contributions.

23. JOHANNES LOHNE, 'Thomas Harriott, the Tycho Brahe of Optics', *Centaurus* 6 (1959) 113–21.
An important but unfortunately neglected article which shows that Hariot was using the law of refraction twenty years before Snell.

24. F. V. MORLEY, 'Thomas Harriot', *Scient. Mon., N.Y.* 14 (1922) 60–66.
A brief, but good account of Hariot's contributions.

25. MARJORIE NICOLSON, 'Kepler, the *Somnium,* and John Donne', *J. Hist. Ideas* 1 (1940) 259–80.

Attempts to show that Hariot may have been a link between Kepler and John Donne.

26. ROBERT PARSONS, *An Advertisement written to a Secretary of My Lord Treasurer of England* (London, 1592).

27. STEPHEN RIGAUD, *Correspondence of Scientific Men of the Seventeenth Century*, 2 vols. (Oxford, 1841).
Contains letters to, from and about Warner, Pell, Barrow, and Newton.

28. STEPHEN RIGAUD, *Supplement to Bradley's Miscellaneous Works* (London, 1833).

29. A. ROBERTSON, 'On Some Mistakes relating to Dr. Bradley's Observations and Hariot's MSS.'. *Edinburgh Philosophical Journal* 6 (1822) 313–18.
Robertson assumes an unhistorical attitude towards Hariot.

30. J. F. SCOTT, *The Mathematical Work of John Wallis* (London, 1938).
Contains an appraisal of Hariot's contributions in the light of Wallis' claims on their behalf.

31. JOHN SHIRLEY, 'Binary Numeration before Leibniz', *Am. J. Phys.* 19 (1951) 452–4.
Hariot experimented with binary and ternary systems long before Leibniz.

32. JOHN SHIRLEY, 'An Early Experimental Determination of Snell's Law', *Am. J. Phys.* 19 (1951) 507–08.
Warner and Aylesbury claimed that Hariot knew Snell's law. Their experimental determination of it was surprisingly modern.

33. HENRY STEVENS, *Thomas Hariot, the Mathematician, the Philosopher, and the Scholar* (London, 1900).
The first attempted biography of Hariot. Leaves much room for improvement.

34. NATHANAEL TORPORLEY, Sion College MSS. ARC 140.2/E10.
Torporley's extant manuscripts on mathematics, physics, astronomy and theology.

35. JOHN WALLIS, *A Treatise of Algebra both Historical and Practical* (London, 1685).
Contains a long section on Hariot's algebra.

36. WALTER WARNER, British Museum Add. MSS. 4425; 4394–96; Sloan MSS. 4458; Harley MSS. 6754–56.
Warner manuscripts on physics, mathematics, philosophy, and biology.

37. NORMAN WILLIAMS, *Sir Walter Ralegh* (London, 1962).
A documentary biography, containing some material on Hariot.

38. ANTHONY À WOOD, see above, II, 42.

39. FRANCES YATES, see above, III, 64.

V.   BACON AND HOBBES (CHAPTERS V, VI)

1. R. I. AARON, 'A Possible Draft of *De Corpore*', *Mind* 54 (1945) 342–56.
Discusses a possible early version of Hobbes' work.

2. FULTON ANDERSON, *The Philosophy of Francis Bacon* (Chicago, 1948).
An excellent, ground-breaking investigation. Contains much material on Bacon's atomism.

3. FRANCIS BACON, *Letters and Life*, J. Spedding, R. Ellis, and D. Heath, 7 vols. (London, 1862–74).

4. FRANCIS BACON, *Works,* ed. J. Spedding, R. Ellis, and D. Heath, 15 vols. (Boston, 1860–4).

5. MARIE BOAS, see above I, 3.

6. MARIE BOAS, 'Bacon and Gilbert', *J. Hist. Ideas* **12** (1951) 466–7.
Miss Boas is puzzled because Bacon criticized Gilbert. It is difficult for her to see how two 'good guys' in the history of science can not have been aware of each other's merits. She suggests that Bacon did not read the 'scientific' *De Magneto* but rather saw only a manuscript version of the less 'scientific' *De Mundo*. Her thesis is unsupported by any weight of evidence. See Roller, V,38.

7. MARIE BOAS, 'Hero's *Pneumatica*: a Study of its Transmission and Influence', *Isis* **40** (1949) 47–48.
An excellent idea, but less well carried out.

8. FRITHIOF BRANDT, *Thomas Hobbes' Mechanical Conception of Nature,* trans. V. Maxwell and A. Fausbell (Copenhagen and London, 1928).
An important work, but rendered almost unreadable by a horrible translation. Available also in Danish.

9. HARCOURT BROWN, 'The Mersenne Correspondence: a Lost Letter by Thomas Hobbes', *Isis* **34** (1943) 311–12.
Concerns Hobbes' views on the void.

10. ROSALIE COLIE, 'Cornelius Drebbel and Salomon de Caus: Two Jacobean Models for Salomon's House', *Huntington Library Quarterly* **18** (1955) 245 60.
Bacon may have found models for his famous scientific house from these two men.

11. A. G. DEBUS, 'The Paracelsian Compromise in Elizabethan England', *Ambix* **8** (1960) 71–97.
On the state of alchemy in late sixteenth-century England.

12. RENÉ DESCARTES, *Oeuvres*, ed. Victor Cousin, 11 vols. (Paris, 1824–6).
Contains the *Principia Philosophiae* rendered into modern French.

13. RENÉ DESCARTES, *Philosophical Works*, ed. E. S. Haldane and G. R. T. Ross, 2 vols. (New York, 1955).
Contains a translation of part of the Descartes correspondence.

14. BENJAMIN FARRINGTON, *Francis Bacon: Philosopher of Industrial Science* (New York, 1961).
Bacon from the Marxist point of view; a laudatory presentation.

15. WALTER FROST, *Bacon und die Naturphilosophie* (Munich, 1927).
Still among the most important examinations of Bacon's natural philosophy.

16. PIERRE GASSEND, *Animadversiones in decimum librum Diogenis Laertii*, 3 vols. (Lyons, 1649).
An important but neglected work in the history of science. Contains a full statement of Gassend's physics.

17. REGINALD GIBSON, *Francis Bacon: a Bibliography of his Works and of Baconiana to the Year 1750* (Oxford, 1950).
A very useful bibliography.

18. Joshua Gregory, 'Chemistry and Alchemy in the Natural Philosophy of Sir Francis Bacon', *Ambix* **2** (1938) 93–111.
    An important search into Bacon as alchemist.

19. Paul Hardacre, 'A Letter from Edmund Waller to Thomas Hobbes', *Huntington Library Quarterly* **11** (1948) 431–3.
    Waller was a personal friend of Hobbes.

20. Charles Harrison, 'Bacon, Hobbes, Boyle and the Ancient Atomists', *Harvard Studies and Notes in Philolophy and Literature* **15** (1933) 191–213.
    An intelligent and ambitious attempt to view Bacon, Hobbes and Boyle in the light of the Epicurean revival of the seventeenth century.

21. Thomas Hobbes, *Elements of Law,* ed. F. Tönnies (Cambridge, 1928).
    Contains, in an appendix, the Little Treatise.

22. Thomas Hobbes, *English Works,* ed. Sir William Molesworth, 11 vols. (London, 1839–45).

23. Thomas Hobbes, *Leviathan,* ed. Michael Oakeshott (Oxford, 1960).

24. Thomas Hobbes, *Opera Philosophica,* ed. Sir William Molesworth, vol. 1 (London, 1839).
    Volume 1 contains Hobbes' Latin autobiography.

25. Jean Jacquot, 'Leviathan et ses critiques anglais au XVIIe siècle', *Thalès* **7** (1951) 92–95.
    A brief note on some controversies stirred by Hobbes.

26. Jean Jacquot, 'Notes on an Unpublished Work of Thomas Hobbes', *Notes Rec. R. Soc. Lond.* **9** (1952) 188–95.
    About an early version of *De Corpore.*

27. Jean Jacquot, 'Un document inedit', *Thalès* **8** (1952) 33–86.
    An early Hobbes manuscript published here for the first time.

28. Alan Keen, *The Private Manuscript Library of Francis Bacon* (London, 1943).
    Little of scientific interest.

29. Max Köhler, 'Die Naturphilosophie von Hobbes und ihre Abhängikeit von Bacon', *Arch. Gesch. Phil.* **15** (1902) 70–91.
    Valuable article by a leading Hobbes scholar.

30. Max Köhler, 'Studien zur Naturphilosophie des Thomas Hobbes', *Arch. Gesch. Phil.* **16** (1902) 59–96.
    Contains Hobbes' views on the void.

31. David Kubrin, 'Spirit and Matter in Hobbes' Mechanical Philosophy', unpublished.
    Kubrin shows that it was many years before Hobbes explicitly called God 'material'.

32. John Laird, *Hobbes* (London, 1934).
    A good sketch, but contains little of scientific interest.

33. Robert Larsen, 'The Aristotelianism of Bacon's *Novum Organum*', *J. Hist. Ideas* **23** (1962) 435–50.
    Larsen shows that Bacon, ostensibly anti-Aristotelian, had roots in scholasticism.

34. Samuel Mintz, 'Galileo, Hobbes and the Circle of Perfection', *Isis* **43** (1952) 98–100.
    Hobbes, like Galileo, was fond of circles.

35. SAMUEL MINTZ, *The Hunting of Leviathan* (Cambridge, 1962).
Hobbes and his critics. Despite some large errors, still valuable.
36. HENRY MORE,*The Immortality of the Soul* (London, 1659).
An important and influential work. Read, and digested, by Newton.
37. J. R. PARTINGTON, see above, I, 16; I, 17.
38. DUANE ROLLER, 'Did Bacon know Gilbert's *De Magnete*?' *Isis* 44 (1953) 466–7.
An answer to Marie Boas (V, 6).
39. SANFORD STRONG, *Catalogue of Letters and other Historical Documents at Welbeck* (London, 1903).
Documents preserved at the Cavendish home. Contains some unpublished Hobbes material.
40. TELESIO, *De Rerum Natura* (Naples, 1570).
A work of natural philosophy which influenced Bacon.
41. FERDINAND TÖNNIES, 'Hobbes Analekten II', *Arch. Gesch. Phil.* 19 (1906) 153–75.
Contains material on Hobbes' views in the 1640's.
42. FERDINAND TÖNNIES, 'Contributions à l'histoire de la pensée de Hobbes', *Archs. Phil.* 12 (1936) 73–98.
Contains material from unpublished Hobbes letters.
43. NEIL VAN DEUSEN, *Telesio* (New York, 1930).
44. ROBERT VAUGHAN, *The Protectorate of Oliver Cromwell*, 2 vols. (London, 1838).
Contains important Pell correspondence.
45. CAY VON BROCKDORFF, *Des Sir Charles Cavendishs Bericht für Joachim Jungius* (Kiel, 1934).
Cavendish's outline of Hobbes' philosophy in the 1640s.
46. MURIEL WEST, 'Notes on the Importance of Alchemy and Modern Science in the Writings of Francis Bacon and Robert Boyle', *Ambix* 9 (1961) 102–14.
Attempts to place the contributions of Bacon and Boyle in an alchemical setting. Valuable as an antidote to those who tend to forget the less 'modern' aspects of seventeenth-century thinkers.

VI. THE MECHANICAL PHILOSOPHY IN FRANCE AND ENGLAND (CHAPTERS VII, VIII)

1. *Actes du congrès du tricentaire de Pierre Gassendi* (Digne, 1957).
2. ANONYMOUS, *The Leveller* (London, 1659), in *Harleian Miscellany*, vol. 4 (London, 1809).
A good summary of Leveller political and religious thought.
3. GEORGES ASCOLI, *La Grande-Bretagne devant l'opinion française au XVIII* siècle, 2 vols. (Paris, 1930).
Contains material on Hobbes, Bacon.
4. JOHN AUBREY, see above, II, 1.

11*

5. ISAAC BARROW, *Theological Works,* ed. Alexander Napier, 9 vols. (Cambridge, 1859).
   Volume 9 contains Barrow's lecture on Cartesianism.
6. *Biographia Britannica,* see above II, 2; II, 3.
7. THOMAS BIRCH, *History of the Royal Society,* 4 vols. (London, 1756–7).
   The minutes of the early meetings.
8. ERNST BLOCH, 'Die chemischen Theorien bei Descartes und den Cartesianern', *Isis* I (1913) 590–636.
   An interesting article, despite Bloch's tendency to see most chemists as Cartesians.
9. MARIE BOAS, see above, I, 3; I, 4.
10. MARIE BOAS, *Robert Boyle and Seventeenth Century Chemistry* (Cambridge, 1958).
    Probably the best scientific biography, but still propagates the same errors concerning Boyle, Gassend, and the mechanical philosophy.
11. J. BOUGEREL, *Vie de Gassendi* (Paris, 1737).
    Still among the most interesting biographies of Gassend.
12. G. S. BRETT, *The Philosophy of Gassendi* (London, 1908).
    Inaccurate and poorly constructed.
13. THOMAS BROWNE, *Pseudodoxia Epidemica* (London, 1648).
14. ROBERT BURTON, *The Anatomy of Melancholy* (Oxford, 1621).
15. E. T. CAMPAGNAC, *The Cambridge Platonists* (Oxford, 1901).
    Selections from their writings.
16. MARGARET CAVENDISH, *Life of William Cavendish, Duke of Newcastle,* ed. C. H. Firth (London, 1906).
    A biography of the patron of the Newcastle Circle by his wife. Later translated into Latin by Charleton.
17. MARGARET CAVENDISH, *Letters and Poems Written in Honour of the Incomparable Princess, Margaret, Dutchess of Newcastle* (London, 1676).
    Contains letters from Constatijn Huygens, Charleton, Glanvill, Hobbes, and others.
18. MARGARET CAVENDISH, *Natures Pictures Drawn by Fancies Pencil to the Life* (London, 1656).
    Contains atomist poems.
19. MARGARET CAVENDISH, *Orations of Divers Sorts* (London, 1662).
    Lady Margaret's views on assorted topics.
20. MARGARET CAVENDISH, *Poems and Fancie* (London, 1653).
    Lady Margaret's first group of atomist poems.
21. MARGARET CAVENDISH, *The Worlds Olio* (London, 1655).
    More of Lady Margaret's natural philosophy.
22. WALTER CHARLETON, *The Darknes of Atheism Refuted by the Light of Nature: a Physico-theologicall Treatise* (London, 1652).
23. WALTER CHARLETON, *Physiologia Epicuro-Gassend-Charltoniana: a Fabrick of Science Natural upon the Hypothesis of Atoms, Founded by Epicurus Repaired by Petrus Gassendus, Augmented by Walter Charleton* (London, 1654).
24. JAN COMENIUS, *Naturall Philosophie Reformed by Divine Light* (London, 1651)

A translation of an earlier work by Comenius. A mélange of alchemical, Aristotelian and atomistic ideas.

25. JACKSON COPE, 'Evelyn, Boyle, and Dr. Wilkinson's Mathematico-Chymico-Mechanical School', *Isis* 50 (1959) 30–32.
    A suggestion for chairs in Cartesian and Gassendist philosophy is traced to a friend of Boyle and of Evelyn.
26. RENÉ DESCARTES, see above, V, 12; V, 13.
27. RENÉ DESCARTES, *Oeuvres de Descartes*, ed. C. Adam and P. Tannery, 13 vol. (Paris, 1897–1913).
28. KENELM DIGBY, *Two Treatises: of Bodies and of Mans Soul* (London, 1669).
    An atomist-Aristotelian mixture.
29. E. J. DIJKSTERHUIS, see above, I, 7.
30. THOMAS EDWARDS, *Gangraena* (London, 1646).
    A book of malicious gossip directed against supposed atheists.
31. EPICURUS, *Morals,* ed. and trans. Walter Charleton (London, 1656).
    Contains an interesting preface by Charleton.
32. JOHN EVELYN, *Essay on the First Book of T. Lucretius Carus De Rerum Natura* (London, 1656).
33. JOHN EVELYN, *Memoirs,* ed. William Bray, 5 vols. (London, 1827).
34. PIERRE GASSEND, see above, V, 16.
35. PIERRE GASSEND, *De Vita et Moribus Epicuri* (Lyons, 1647).
36. PIERRE GASSEND, *Opera Omnia*, 6 vols. (Lyons, 1658).
37. ALLAN GEWIRTZ, 'Experience and the Non-mathematical in the Cartesian Method', *J. Hist. Ideas* 2 (1941) 183–210.
38. DOUGLAS GRANT, *Margaret the First* (London, 1957).
    A good biography of Margaret Cavendish, Duchess of Newcastle.
39. A. R. HALL, see above, II, 17.
40. J. O. HALLIWELL, see above, IV, 11.
41. PAUL HARDACRE, 'Royalists in Exile, 1642–1660', *Huntington Library Quarterly* 16 (1953) 353–70.
    Contains some information on the Cavendishes.
42. CHARLES HARRISON, see above, I, 11.
43. HELEN HERVEY, see above, IV, 15.
44. THOMAS HOBBES, *A Minute or first Draught of the Optiques* (Paris, 1647).
    British Museum Harley MS. 3360.
    A complete treatise on optics by Hobbes, unpublished.
45. THOMAS HOBBES, see above, V, 22; V, 24.
46. GUY HOLLAND, *The Grand Prerogative of Humane Nature* (London, 1653).
47. ROBERT HOOKE, *The Posthumous Works of Robert Hooke, M.D., S.R.S.,* ed. Richard Waller (London, 1705).
48. JEAN JACQUOT, 'Sir Charles Cavendish and his Learned Friends', *Ann. Sci.* 8 (1952) 13–28; 175–92.
    The first examination of what has, in this dissertation, been called the Newcastle Circle.
49. RICHARD FOSTER JONES, 'Puritanism, Science and Christ Church', *Isis* 31 (1939) 65–67.

Describes an anonymous suggestion for the establishment of chairs in Gassendist and Cartesian philosophies. See Cope, VI, 24.

50. WILBUR JORDAN, see above, II, 23.

51. ROBERT KARGON, 'Walter Charleton, Robert Boyle and the Acceptance of Epicurean Atomism in England', *Isis* **55** (1964) 184–92.
An attempt to delineate the early reception of atomism in England in the 1650's, showing the contributions of Charleton and Boyle.

52. ROBERT KARGON, 'William Petty's Mechanical Philosophy', *Isis* **56** (1965) 63–66.
Petty as a case study in the establishment of the mechanical philosophy.

53. STERLING LAMPRECHT, 'The Role of Descartes in Seventeenth Century England', in *Studies in the History of Ideas*, vol. 3 (New York, 1935), pp. 181–242.

54. ROBERT LENOBLE, *Mersenne ou la naissance du mécanisme* (Paris, 1943).
An excellent study of the revival of the mechanical philosophy in the mid-seventeenth century. Unfortunately neglects the Englishmen who are so important for this book.

55. ROBERT LINDSAY, 'Pierre Gassendi and the Revival of Atomism in the Renaissance', *Am. J. Phys.* **13** (1945) 235–42.
A good introductory article.

56. THOMAS MAYO, see above, I, 15.

57. GERALD MEYER, *The Scientific Lady in England: 1650–1760* (Berkeley, Cal., 1955).
Contains some material on Margaret Cavendish.

58. WYNDHAM MILES, 'Sir Kenelm Digby, Alchemist, Scholar, Courtier, and Man of Adventure', *Chymia* **2** (1949) 119–28.
A broad look at Digby. Not useful for his atomism.

59. SAMUEL MINTZ, 'The Duchess of Newcastle's Visit to the Royal Society', *Journal of English and German Philology* **51** (1952) 168–76.

60. HENRY MORE, *A Collection of Several Philosophical Writings* (London, 1662).
Contains the *Antidote against Atheism*, which has been compared with 1653 edition, although the latter has not been used extensively.

61. MARJORIE NICOLSON, 'The Early Stage of Cartesianism in England', *Studies in Philology* **26** (1929) 45–74.
Contains much valuable information on this important topic, although it is far from a definitive article.

62. PERCY OSMOND, *Isaac Barrow, his Life and Times* (London, 1944).
A mediocre and sketchy biography.

63. RICHARD OVERTON, *Mans Mortallitie* (Amsterdam, 1643).
An important work for the intellectual history of the seventeenth century. Curiously overlooked by almost all historians of science.

64. SAMUEL PEPYS, *Diary*, ed. H. B. Wheatley, 6 vols. (London, 1893–9).

65. R. T. PETERSSON, *Sir Kenelm Digby* (Cambridge, Mass, 1956).
A good biography using much unpublished material.

66. HENRY PERRY, *The First Duchess of Newcastle and Husband as Figures in Literary History* (Boston, 1918).
Less valuable than Grant's biography of the Duchess, but still worth while.

67. WILLIAM PETTY, *A discourse made before the Royal Society Concerning the Use of Duplicate Proportion . . . together with a new Hypothesis of Springy of Elastique Motion* (London, 1674).
A good example of the hypothetical physics in transition to a more mathematical physics.

68. RICHARD POPKIN, *The History of Scepticism from Erasmus to Descartes* (Assen, 1960).

69. HENRY POWER, *Experimental Philosophy* (London, 1664).

70. JOHN ROBERTS, *A Short History of Freethought,* 2 vols. (London, 1906).
A valuable, albeit partisan, account.

71. BERNARD ROCHOT, *Les travaux de Gassendi sur Epicure et sur l'atomisme 1619–1658* (Paris, 1944).
An elaborate bibliographical essay.

72. HUMPHREY ROLLESTON, 'Walter Charleton, D.M., F.R.C.P., F.R.S.'. *Bull. Hist. Med.* **8** (1940) 403–16.
A brief biographical sketch which does not go far beyond the D.N.B.

73. DANTON SAILOR, 'Cudworth and Descartes', *J. Hist. Ideas* **23** (1961) 133–40.
Cudworth as a Cartesian. Lacks depth.

74. DENIS SAURAT, *Milton et le matérialisme chrétien en Angleterre* (Paris, 1928).
Contains a good section on Overton.

75. J. E. SAVESON, 'Descartes' Influence on John Smith, Cambridge Platonist', *J. Hist. Ideas* **20** (1959) 259–73.
Examines the Cartesianism of an important Cambridge Platonist.

76. J. E. SAVESON, 'Differing Reactions to Descartes among the Cambridge Platonists', *J. Hist. Ideas* **21** (1960) 560–7.
A good attempt to investigate the complex reception of Descartes in England.

77. JOHN SMITH, *Select Discourses* (London, 1660).
Sermons and lectures published posthumously.

78. NORMAN KEMP SMITH, *New Studies in the Philosophy of Descartes* (London, 1952).

79. GASTON SORTAIS, see above, I, 18.

80. DOROTHY STIMSON, *Scientists and Amateurs* (New York, 1948).
The only full length modern history of the Royal Society.

81. JOHN STOYE, *English Travelers Abroad 1604–67: Their Influence in English Society and Politics* (London, 1952).
Useful for a picture of emigré activities.

82. F. S. TAYLOR, 'The Chemical Studies of John Evelyn', *Ann. Sci.* **8** (1952) 285–92.
An account of Evelyn's chemistry and his dependence on Annibel Barlet. No atomism.

83. ANDREW VAN MELSEN, see above, I, 20.

84. ROBERT VAUGHAN, see above, V, 44.

85. JOHN WARD, *Lives of the Gresham Proffessors* (London, 1740).

86. RICHARD WESTFALL, 'The Foundations of Newton's Philosophy of Nature', *Br. J. hist. Sci.* **1** (1962) 171–82.
An excellent examination of Newton's early notebooks.

87. GEORGE WILLIAMSON, 'Milton and the Mortalist Heresy', *Studies in Philology* **32** (1935) 553–79.
Excellent survey of the spirit-matter controversy in the 1650s.

88. ANTHONY À WOOD, see above, II, 42.

VII. BOYLE, NEWTON AND THE NEWTONIANS
(CHAPTERS IX–XI)

1. WILBUR APPLEBAUM, 'Boyle and Hobbes: a Reconsideration', *J. Hist. Ideas* **25** (1964) 117–19.
A correction of Robert Greene, VII, 34.

2. FRANCIS BACON, see above, V, 4.

3. ISAAC BARROW, *Mathematical Lectures Read in the Publick Schools*, trans. John Kirby (London, 1734).
An important, and forgotten, series of lectures by Newton's mentor.

4. ISAAC BARROW, see above, VI, 5.

5. RICHARD BAXTER, *The Nature and Immortality of the Soul* (London, 1682).

6. RICHARD BAXTER, *The Reasons of the Christian Religion* (London, 1667).

7. MURIEL BENTHAM, 'Some 17th Century Views concerning the Nature of Heat and Cold', *Ann. Sci.* **2** (1937) 431–58.
Good survey of the views of De Rampalle, Mariotte, Boyle, *et al.*

8. RICHARD BENTLEY, *Correspondence*, 2 vols. (London, 1842).
Bentley's lectures are printed in Newton, VII, 79.

9. *Bibliothèque universelle et historique*, ser. 1, **8** (1688) 436.
An unsigned review of Newton's *Principia*.

10. OTTO BLÜH, 'Newton and Spinoza', *Nature, Lond.* **135** (1936) 658–9.
A brief suggestion of a link.

11. MARIE BOAS, see above, I, 3; I, 4; V, 7; VI, 10.

12. MARIE BOAS, 'Boyle as a Theoretical Scientist', *Isis* **41** (1950) 261–8.
According to Miss Boas, the mechanical philosophy culminates in the work of Boyle.

13. ROBERT BOYLE, *The Works of the Honourable Robert Boyle*, ed. Thomas Birch, 6 vols. (London, 1772).
Contains a life of Boyle by Birch.

14. EDWIN A. BURTT, *The Metaphysical Foundations of Modern Physical Science* (New York, n.d.).
A classical work, stimulating and valuable. This dissertation disagrees, however, on many major points.

15. *Cambridge University* Additional Manuscripts 3996.
Newton's early notebooks.

16. MARGARET CAVENDISH, see above, VI, 20.

17. SAMUEL CLARKE, *Leibniz-Clarke Correspondence*, ed. H. G. Alexander (Manchester, 1956).

18. SAMUEL CLARKE, *Works*, 4 vols. (London, 1738).

19. I. B. COHEN, *Franklin and Newton* (Philadelphia, 1956).
Best on Franklin. Good bibliography.

20. I. B. COHEN, 'Newton in the Light of Recent Scholarship', *Isis* **51** (1960) 489–514.
    Very helpful source of recent bibliography.
21. JACKSON COPE, see above, VI, 25.
22. RALPH CUDWORTH, *True Intellectual System of the Universe,* ed. Thomas Birch, 4 vols. (London, 1820).
23. RICHARD EHRENFELD, *Grundriss einer Entwicklungsgeschichte der chemischen Atomistik* (Heidelberg, 1906).
    Contains a chapter on Boyle's dependence on Descartes and Gassend.
24. HAROLD FISCH, 'The Scientist as Priest: A Note on Robert Boyle's Natural Theology', *Isis* **44** (1953) 252–65.
25. MITCHELL FISHER, *Robert Boyle: Devout Naturalist* (Philadelphia, 1945).
    Good study of Boyle as a theologian.
26. R. T. FORBES, 'Was Newton an Alchemist?' *Chymia* **2** (1949) 27–36.
    The chemical basis of Newton's atomism discussed.
27. JOHN FULTON, *A Bibilography of the Honourable Robert Boyle,* 2nd ed. (Oxford, 1961.)
    A very useful bibliography.
28. PIERRE GASSEND, see above, V, 16; VI, 36.
29. JOSEPH GLANVILL, *Essays on several important subjects in philosophy and religion* (London, 1676).
30. JOSEPH GLANVILL, *Philosophia pia* (London, 1671).
31. JOSEPH GLANVILL, *A Praefatory Answer to Mr. Henry Stubbe* (London, 1671).
32. JOSEPH GLANVILL, *Scepsis scientifica* (London, 1665).
33. DOUGLAS GRANT, see above, VI, 38.
34. ROBERT A. GREENE, 'Henry More and Robert Boyle on the Spirit of Nature', *J. Hist. Ideas* **23** (1962) 45–74.
    Rather naïve and superficial.
35. WILLIAM J. GREENSTREET, *Isaac Newton: 1642–1727* (London, 1927).
    A collection of essays of varying utility.
36. HENRY GUERLAC, 'Francis Hauksbee: expérimenteur au profit de Newton', *Archs. int. Hist. Sci.* **16** (1963) 113–28.
    Proposes a possible reason for Newton's aether suggestion.
37. HENRY GUERLAC, *Newton et Epicure* (Paris, Palais de la Découverte, 1963).
    Newton in the setting of the Epicurean revival.
38. A. R. HALL, 'Newton's First Book', *Archs int. Hist. Sci.* **13** (1960) 39–61.
39. A. R. HALL, 'Sir Isaac Newton's Notebook 1661–65', *Camb. hist. J.* **9** (1948) 239–50.
40. A. R. HALL and MARIE BOAS HALL, 'Clarke and Newton', *Isis* **52** (1961) 583–5.
    In support of Koyre's contention that Clarke was Newton's spokesman.
41. A. R. HALL and MARIE BOAS HALL, 'Newton's Chemical Experiments', *Archs int. Hist. Sci.,* **11** (1958), 113–52.
42. A. R. HALL and MARIE BOAS HALL, 'Newton's Mechanical Principles', *J. Hist. Ideas* **20** (1959) 167–78.
    Newton as a mechanical philosopher. See also the essay in Newton, VII, 83.

43. A. R. HALL and MARIE BOAS HALL, 'Newton's Theory of Matter', *Isis* **51** (1960) 131–4.
Accepts everything Newton wrote as having equal weight despite his protests to the contrary.

44. MARIE BOAS HALL, *Robert Boyle on Natural Philosophy* (Bloomington, Ind., 1965).

45. EDMUND HALLEY, 'Some Queries concerning the Nature of Light and Diaphanous Bodies', *Phil. Trans. R. Soc.* **17** (1693) 998–9.

46. JOHN HARRIS. *Lexicon Technicum* (London, 1704). Second edition, 1708. Fifth edition, 1736.

47. Historical Manuscript Commission, see above, IV, 16.

48. THOMAS HOBBES, see above, V, 22.

49. ROBERT HOOKE, *Micrographia* (London, 1665).

50. RICHARD HUNT, *The Place of Religion in the Science of Robert Boyle* (Pittsburgh, 1955).
An uninspired investigation.

51. GEORGE HUXLEY, 'Roger Cotes and Natural Philosophy', *Scr. math.* **26** (1963) 231–8.
The only article on Cotes. Useful, but should be expanded.

52. RICHARD FOSTER JONES, see above, VI, 49.

53. *Journal des Scavans,* **16**(1688) 237–38.
A review of Newton's Principia.

54. ROBERT KARGON, see above, VI, 51.

55. ALEXANDRE KOYRÉ, 'Hypothèse et expérience chez Newton', *Bull. Soc. fr. Phil.* **50** (1956) 59–79.

56. ALEXANDRE KOYRÉ, 'Les Queries de l'Optique', *Archs int. Hist. Sci.* **13** (1960) 15–29.
Poses challenging questions which have yet to be answered about the changes in the 'queries'.

57. ALEXANDRE KOYRÉ, 'Les Regulae Philosophandi', *Archs int. Hist. Sci.* **13** (1960) 3–14.
Some important changes in the rules of reasoning between editions.

58. ALEXANDER KOYRÉ, *Newtonian Studies* (Cambridge, Mass., 1965).
Stimulating, perceptive essays collected for the first time. For Newton on hypothesis, see 'Concept and Experience in Newton's Scientific Thought'.

59. ALEXANDRE KOYRÉ, 'The Significance of the Newtonian Synthesis', *Archs int. Hist. Sci.* **3** (1950) 291–311.
A broad look at the Newtonian achievement.

60. ALEXANDRÉ KOYRÉ and I. B. COHEN, 'The Case of the Missing Tanquam: Leibniz, Newton, and Clarke', *Isis* **52** (1961) 555–66.
Newton's missing 'as if' causes Leibniz consternation.

61. THOMAS KUHN, 'Robert Boyle and Structural Chemistry', *Isis* **43**(1952)12–36.
Boyle's views on elements and compounds not so modern as is usually thought.

62. JOHANNES LOHNE, 'Newton's Proof of the Sine Law and his Mathematical Principles of Colors', *Archs Hist. exact. Sci.* **1** (1961) 389–405.

63. Douglas McKie, 'Some Notes on Newton's Chemical Philosophy Written Upon the Occasion of the Tercentenary of his Birth', *Phil. Mag.* **33** (1942) 847–70.
A fair summary of Newton's chemical views.
64. Robert McRae, 'The Unity of the Sciences: Bacon, Descartes, and Leibniz', *J. Hist. Ideas* **18** (1957) 27–48.
65. Johannes Magnenus, *Democritus Reviviscens* (Leiden, 1648).
First published in 1646.
66. Maurice Mandelbaum, *Philosophy, Science and Sense Perception* (Baltimore, 1964).
Contains valuable insights concerning Boyle and Newton and their views of the corpuscularian path to knowledge.
67. Hélène Metzger, *Attraction universelle et religion nuturelle chez quelques commentateurs anglais de Newton* (Paris, 1938).
68. E. C. Millington, 'Theories of Cohesion in the 17th Century', *Ann. Sci.* **5** (1945) 253–69.
Contains some material on atomism. Rather prosaic.
69. Henry More, see above, VI, 60.
70. Louis T. More, 'Boyle as Alchemist', *J. Hist. Ideas* **2** (1941) 61–76.
Welcome attempt to place Boyle in his seventeenth-century context.
71. Louis T. More, *The Life and Works of the Honorable Robert Boyle* (New York, 1944).
Not up to the standard of his life of Newton.
72. Isaac Newton, *Correspondence,* ed. H. W. Turnbull, 3 vols. (Cambridge, 1959–61).
73. Isaac Newton, *Mathematical Principles of Natural Philosophy,* trans. A. Motte, revised F. Cajori (Berkeley, 1962).
Based on the third edition.
74. Isaac Newton, *Optice,* trans. S. Clarke (London, 1706).
75. Isaac Newton, *Opticks* (London, 1704).
The first edition. Contains no queries.
76. Isaac Newton, *Opticks,* 2nd ed. (London, 1718).
77. Isaac Newton, *Opticks,* 3rd ed. (London, 1721).
78. Isaac Newton, *Opticks,* 4th ed. (New York, 1952).
79. Isaac Newton, *Papers and Letters on Natural Philosophy,* ed. I. B. Cohen (Cambridge, Mass., 1958).
80. Isaac Newton, *Philosophiae naturalis principia mathematica* (London, 1687).
The first edition.
81. Isaac Newton, *Philosophiae naturalis principia mathematica,* 2nd ed. (London, 1713).
82. Isaac Newton, *Philosophiae naturalis principia mathematica,* 3rd ed. (London, 1723).
83. Isaac Newton, *Unpublished Scientific Papers,* ed. A. R. Hall and M. B. Hall (Cambridge, 1962).
Contains several introductory essays by the Halls.

162 *Selected Bibliography*

84. JOHN NEWTON, *The English Academy,* 2nd ed.(London, 1693).
A review of current texts.
85. HENRY OLDENBURG, Epistle dedicatory to Boyle, *Phil. Trans. R. Soc.* 5 (1670) 1143–6.
86. HENRY OLDENBURG, 'Preface', *Phil. Trans. R. Soc.* 6 (1671) 2089.
87. SAMUEL PARKER, *A Demonstration of the Divine Authority of the Law of Nature and of the Christian Religion*(London, 1681).
88. SAMUEL PARKER, *A Free and Impartial Censure of the Platonick Philosophie,* 2nd ed.(Oxford, 1667).
89. JACQUES ROHAULT, *System of Natural Philosophy, Illustrated with Dr. Samuel Clark's Notes, taken mostly out of Sir Isaac Newton's Philosophy,* trans. J. Clarke, 2 vols. (London, 1723).
Cartesian physics with Newtonian footnotes by Samuel Clarke.
90. *Royal Society Newton Tercentenary Celebrations* (Cambridge, 1947).
Essays of varying utility.
91. DANTON SAILOR, 'Moses and Atomism', *J. Hist. Ideas* 25 (1964) 3–16.
An attempt to trace the purification of atomism by attributing the theory to Moses. Handled in a rather unimaginative way.
92. A. J. SNOW, *Matter and Gravity in Newton's Physical Philosophy* (London, 1926).
Rather too enthusiastic in making Newton a disciple of Gassend.
93. DOROTHY STIMSON, see above, VI, 80.
94. EDWARD STRONG, 'Newtonian Explications of Natural Philosophy', *J. Hist. Ideas* 18 (1957) 49–83.
95. EDWARD STRONG, 'Newton's Mathematical Way', *J. Hist. Ideas* 12 (1951), 90–110.
Strong presents a view differing from the one offered in this dissertation.
96. A. S. TURBERVILLE, *History of Welbeck Abbey and its Owners,* 2 vols.(London, 1938).
Good section on the Duke and Duchess of Newcastle.
97. S. I. VAVILOV, 'Newton and the Atomic Theory', in *Royal Society Newton Tercentenary Celebrations,* VII, 90.
98. RICHARD WESTFALL, see above, VI, 86.
99. RICHARD WESTFALL, 'Newton and his Critics on the Nature of Colours', *Archs int. Hist. Sci.* 15 (1962) 41–58.
Interesting attempt to re-evaluate the controversy over Newton's optical papers. Assumes a position quite different from that of this dissertation.
100. RICHARD WESTFALL, 'Newton's Reply to Hooke and the Theory of Colour', *Isis* 54 (1963) 82–96.
101. RICHARD WESTFALL, 'Unpublished Boyle Papers Relating to Scientific Method', *Ann. Sci.* 12 (1956) 63–73, 103–17.
Westfall published for the first time an early Boyle manuscript on atoms.
102. PHILIP WIENER, 'The Experimental Philosophy of Robert Boyle(1626–91)', *Phil. Rev.* 41 (1932) 594–609.
Claims, and probably rightly, that the seventeenth century misunderstood Aristotelianism.

103. DEREK WHITESIDE, 'The Expanding World of Newtonian Research', *Hist. Sci.* **1** (1962) 16–29.
Contains some recent bibliography.

104. W. WIGHTMAN, 'David Gregory's Commentary on Newton's *Principia*', *Nature, Lond.* **179** (1957) 393–4.
The reactions of an early Newtonian.

105. THOMAS WISE, *A Confutation of the Reason and Philosophy of Atheism.* 2 vols. (London, 1706).
Concerned with the purification of atomism.

INDEX